Energy is an issue that touches every person on the planet.

The Great
Energy Challenge

**Be part of the solution.
Take part in the challenge.**

is a National Geographic initiative in partnership with Shell that convenes and engages influential citizens and key energy stakeholders in solutions-based thinking and dialogue about our shared energy future. It's a call-to-action to become actively involved, to learn more and do more—to change how we think about and consume energy so that we can all help tackle the big energy questions. Let's start now.

Stay informed with up-to-the-minute news and insights
ENERGY NEWS ▶ Trusted, balanced, independent global reporting with a scope and scale that stands apart.

Test Your Energy I.Q.
ENERGY QUIZZES ▶ Featuring amazing facts and energy-saving tips.

Join the debate and move the conversation forward
THE BIG ENERGY QUESTION ▶ Encouraging solutions through diverse conversations.

Engage with the world's experts
ENERGY BLOG ▶ A fascinating forum where experts keep issues front and center.

How will we drive change for smarter mobility?

Do rapidly growing cities offer a blueprint for energy sustainability?

As we move to a population of 9 billion by mid-century, how do we manage the stress on the intersection of food, water, and energy?

What are the breakthroughs and new technologies that will enter the energy mix?

Everything you need to stay current on the big picture of energy— and what it means for you—can be found at

greatenergychallenge.com

 NATIONAL GEOGRAPHIC

A NATIONAL GEOGRAPHIC INITIATIVE IN PARTNERSHIP WITH SHELL

NATIONAL GEOGRAPHIC

VOL. 225 • NO. 2

58

FEBRUARY 2014

On the Cover
The colorized fibers connect different regions of the brain.
Magnetic resonance image by Van Wedeen and L. L. Wald, Martinos Center for Biomedical Imaging, Human Connectome Project

Contributions to the National Geographic Society are tax deductible under Section 501(c)(3) of the U.S. tax code.

FOR SUBSCRIPTIONS, GIFT MEMBERSHIPS, OR CHANGES OF ADDRESS, CONTACT CUSTOMER SERVICE AT NGMSERVICE.COM OR CALL 1-800-NGS-LINE (647-5463). OUTSIDE THE U.S. AND CANADA PLEASE CALL +1-813-979-6845.

PRINTED ON 100% PEFC-CERTIFIED PAPER

 Please recycle.

OFFICIAL JOURNAL OF THE NATIONAL GEOGRAPHIC SOCIETY

A Prairie Home

A few years ago I was in the middle of a meeting when one of our senior editors ushered in a tall man with a large, expressive face, wearing owlish glasses and dressed in a khaki suit. In a voice once described as "a baritone that seems precision-engineered to narrate a documentary about glaciers," he addressed the group and pitched a story idea. He wanted, he told us, to do a story about his own "personal geography." That man was the author, radio personality, and story-teller Garrison Keillor, and there could be only one answer to the appeal.

It's a piece he's been writing his whole life.

Keillor's reminiscence, "There's No Place Like Home," is the result. You might say it's a piece he's been writing his whole life. Ostensibly, it's about Minneapolis-St. Paul. He conjures word pictures of neighborhoods with stucco bungalows, lakes with names like Minnetonka and Nokomis, and the sweep of the rocket tail fins on a white Cadillac convertible. But it's also something different and very special.

Keillor's piece is an interior geog-raphy; it's the map of a man's soul. In summoning up the Twin Cities of his youth and adulthood, he talks about what it means to be not just from a place, but *of* a place. Early on, he says, he realized that Minneapolis-St. Paul was a much better place than Manhat-tan in which to be an original. In his essay Keillor tells us why where you come from matters. "If you want to know the truth," he says, "I feel understood there."

Keillor likes driving rural Minnesota roads. "One evening," says photogra-pher Erika Larsen, "I went along." She shot this near Buffalo Lake.

125 Years of Photos

As a college junior in 1976, I was an avid photographer. (How I miss my Pentax SP1000!) I wrote to *National Geographic* asking the requirements to be a staff photographer. I received a personal reply stating I would need to have a college degree and five years' experience on a photo-oriented news-paper, and I probably should know another language. It also stated that "the average *Geographic* photographer spends far more time being a traveler, diplomat, making arrangements, and coping with a myriad of problems that can arise when he or she is working alone in a strange land."

NANCY J. BUSHNELL
North Mankato, Minnesota

To Robert Draper: I'm sorry. You are wrong. You are not "just one of the writers." Your article on the power of photography moved me as much as the photographs themselves.

FAITH PARKER
Saratoga Springs, New York

Before the Civil War, when the art form was still in its infancy, photographs were seen as inherently unsuitable for recording events because of the mere split second of captured time. Lithographs were far more popular because they could be crafted to suit current tastes in public memory. The modern mentality is far different.

BRIAN DOLPHIN
Columbia, South Carolina

Reading Sharbat Gula's story and learning about her life helped me understand why I could never forget her face. I could see the determination and fear in her eyes, a combination of vulnerability and strength that is so difficult to capture. This photograph by Steve McCurry is a reminder of human endurance regardless of gender, age, or culture.

CRISTINA GOSSEREZ-SEELYE
Weston, Florida

Enough of the Afghan Girl already. We don't want to see her anymore.

MARC BERNSTEIN
New York, New York

With banks of yellow-spine magazines on the shelves behind me, dating back to the days of Koda-chrome and before, at the age of 84 I doubted that renewing my annual subscription would still inspire my photographic and world interests. Then your October Photo Issue arrived. Thank you for a new lease of life.

HARRY BARKER
Lancashire, England

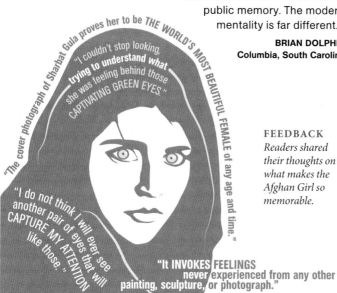

"The cover photograph of Sharbat Gula proves her to be THE WORLD'S MOST BEAUTIFUL FEMALE of any age and time."

"I couldn't stop looking, trying to understand what she was feeling behind those CAPTIVATING GREEN EYES."

"I do not think I will ever see another pair of eyes that will CAPTURE MY ATTENTION like those."

"It INVOKES FEELINGS never experienced from any other painting, sculpture, or photograph."

FEEDBACK
Readers shared their thoughts on what makes the Afghan Girl so memorable.

Corrections

OCTOBER 2013, THE PRICE OF PRECIOUS
The graphic on page 56 is incorrectly labeled. It should read "Number of personal electronics owned by adults in the U.S." In addition, five million is the metropolitan area population of Atlanta, not the population of the city proper.

EMAIL comments to ngsforum@ngm.com; for subscription help, ngsline@customersvc.com.

TWITTER @NatGeoMag

WRITE National Geographic Magazine, PO Box 98199, Washington, DC 20090-8199. Letters may be edited for clarity and length.

ART: DANIELA SANTAMARINA, NGM STAFF
BASED ON A PHOTO BY STEVE McCURRY

Jason De León
National Geographic
Emerging Explorer

EXPERTISE
Cultural Anthropologist

LOCATION
Arizona

Border Lines

My team studies what happens to undocumented migrants crossing the border from Mexico to the U.S. Many don't make it. So the archaeology and anthropology we do are often unpleasant—uncovering death and physical and emotional suffering. We hope the research that we do can aid immigration law reform.

On a trip to study a four-year-old migrant site where the traffic had slowed, we found the body of a 41-year-old woman. She was just south of Tucson, Arizona, in the Sonoran Desert, only 30 miles from the Mexican border. The area is mountainous. She had been cresting a steep hill. It was July, and the temperatures there averaged 100°F or more.

Finding a person meant the team had to navigate between gathering scientific data and feeling empathy. And we had to call the police. She'd been dead about four days, and there were already birds circling overhead. We knew what animals did to bodies in the desert, so we needed to collect what data we could—without disturbing the body—then and there.

There were seven of us on the team, and we were all struggling. It was easier when we had seen other migrants' bodies that were fragmented, a collection of bones. No one wanted to take this woman's photograph because we could see her humanity. We called her Marisol.

Before we found her, we had come across some items buried under a tree nearby, including a backpack with a new, very vibrant Mexican blanket inside. When we finished logging the data—what she carried with her, her clothing, the GPS coordinates—we used the blanket to cover Marisol up and waited for the police. It was a temporary gesture.

ART: ISTVAN BANYAI. PHOTO: MICHAEL WELLS

Canon

ZOOM IN ON
WILDLIFE

One of the best ways to capture beautiful, natural images of wildlife is to give your subject room— by using a zoom.

"I rounded a corner at my local zoo just as this peacock fanned its tail. It was completely unexpected, and I wanted my photograph to capture that sense of surprise. Luckily my Canon PowerShot SX280 HS didn't disappoint. I used the high optical zoom and let the feathers fill the frame to add impact. Getting this level of stunning color and detail from a compact camera is amazing. And since it fits in my pocket, I'm more likely to have it with me when a moment like this unfolds.

The SX280's powerful zoom also lets me stay back and not distract my subject—essential if you want natural-looking wildlife shots. It stretches my creativity too, letting me experiment and change composition fast, moving in on a leopard's spots or a snake's scales. And with the touch of a button, I shifted to full HD video and stereo sound and captured hippos splashing in the water and the roar of a lion. Wi-Fi compatibility makes sharing images and comments easy, and since the GPS function records the time and location of every shot, I can retrace my steps after a trip. My advice? Don't rush; wait for wildlife to move into the right position. Make sure background elements don't detract from your main focus. Get creative with the zoom. And have the PowerShot SX280 HS in your pocket."

Canon PowerShot SX280 HS

f

VISIONS

Iceland
The colorful rhyolite mountains of the Land-mannalaugar highlands are a popular hiking destination in Iceland's southern interior. Getting there can be hard: Local roads aren't paved, and rivers run across them. They must be forded using four-wheel drive.

PHOTO: HANS STRAND

Bhutan
Robes fly as monks practice a traditional dance in the courtyard of the Rinpung Dzong, a fortress and monastery complex dating from 1646—and now a seat of district government—located in Bhutan's Paro Valley.

PHOTO: DAVID BUTOW

VISIONS | YOUR SHOT

This page features two photographs: one chosen by our editors and one chosen by our readers via online voting. For more information, go to *yourshot.nationalgeographic.com.*

EDITORS' CHOICE

Hong Ng CK
Kuala Lumpur, Malaysia

In the Dang district of Nepal, Hong was working with an organization that holds free art classes for young students. During a break, a girl began jumping rope, sending dust from the floor into the air as the sun shone in through a window behind her.

READERS' CHOICE

Aleš Umek
Celje, Slovenia

Umek rode his bike 55 miles to take landscape shots of Slovenia's picturesque Logar Valley. "I wanted to make a dream landscape," he says. At the top of one hill he found a view of a small homestead that looked as if it belonged in a fairy tale.

How long will an elephant live? Look to its teeth.

Area enlarged

PHOTOS: HUGH TURVEY. GRAPHIC: JOSÉ MIGUEL MAYO. SOURCE: DAVID FAGAN, THE COLYER INSTITUTE

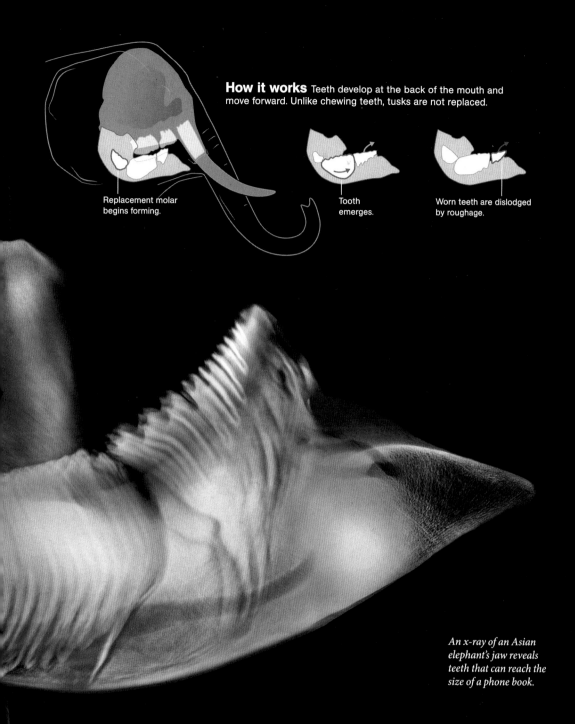

How it works Teeth develop at the back of the mouth and move forward. Unlike chewing teeth, tusks are not replaced.

Replacement molar begins forming.

Tooth emerges.

Worn teeth are dislodged by roughage.

An x-ray of an Asian elephant's jaw reveals teeth that can reach the size of a phone book.

TEETH MAY BE the most essential organ elephants have, says veterinary dentist David Fagan. The reason is appetite. An African savanna elephant consumes between 400 and 600 pounds of vegetation a day, an Asian elephant about 300. To process that quantity of food, elephants need to chew constantly. They wear down each tooth until it's no longer useful. Then it falls out.

Most other mammals have two sets of teeth in their lifetimes. Elephants go through six. Each set—one tooth on the top, one on the bottom—lasts about three years when an African savanna elephant is young but can be good for more than ten years later in life. Unlike human teeth, which sprout from the gum line, elephants' start at the back of the mouth and move forward like a conveyor belt.

It's an effective system until there aren't any teeth left. Elephants that live to old age—about 70 years in captivity—often succumb to starvation, unable to chew. —*Daniel Stone*

Rooftop Refuge

Up to 5,000 people are in Westport, Washington, on a summer day. About a fifth could be too close to the coast and too far from high ground to escape on foot from a tsunami, which experts say would follow an earthquake there by 25 minutes. The city is forging a safe haven, building on state plans. Last April it approved a bond for the first vertical tsunami refuge in the U.S.—on top of a school and able to withstand a 9.2 magnitude earthquake.

"Japan's 2011 tsunami was a transitional moment in moving Westport from planning to implementation," says emergency manager John Schelling. Westport residents saw parallels between the Japanese towns and their own area: both in a potential tsunami path, both flat. So when Westport needed a new school, a tsunami plan became part of it. Rising a little taller than 55 feet, the building will allow water to pass through without compromising the structure, which can shelter 700. Planners hope that this first successful idea spawns other refuge options. —*Johnna Rizzo*

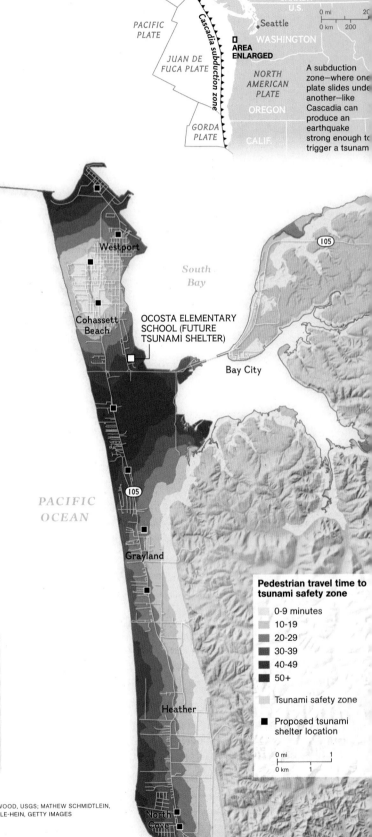

A subduction zone—where one plate slides under another—like Cascadia can produce an earthquake strong enough to trigger a tsunam

OCOSTA ELEMENTARY SCHOOL (FUTURE TSUNAMI SHELTER)

Pedestrian travel time to tsunami safety zone

- 0-9 minutes
- 10-19
- 20-29
- 30-39
- 40-49
- 50+

Tsunami safety zone

■ Proposed tsunami shelter location

MAP: JEROME N. COOKSON, NGM STAFF. SOURCES: NATHAN WOOD, USGS; MATHEW SCHMIDTLEIN, CALIFORNIA STATE UNIVERSITY, SACRAMENTO. PHOTO: N EISELE-HEIN, GETTY IMAGES

NEXT

In some wasp species, such as yellow jackets and hornets, females have 12 antennal segments. The males have 13.

Fingertips grip wet objects, like this marble, better when they're "pruney."

Silent Flight

German engineers have a flight plan: mimic barn owls' quiet aerial maneuvering to make less noisy airfoils for human aviation. Nocturnal hunters, barn owls use acoustics to locate prey, so they can't be distracted by noises of their own making.

Key to a barn owl's stealth is flying slowly, with very little flapping. Its steep wing curve is a particular asset: It's especially good at creating the low pressure on the top side that sucks the wings upward, says lead researcher Thomas Bachmann. Plumage plays a part too. Owls have extremely dense coats, and their feathers' soft texture muffles sound. Fringes on the edges of feathers may also lead to ways to downplay turbulence. —*Johnna Rizzo*

Solid Grasp

Linger in the bathtub long enough, and fingers and toes will prune. Those wrinkles may seem insignificant, but they could be rooted in evolution.

Puckered digits were once thought to be just the bloated result of water absorption. Then Newcastle University evolutionary biologist Tom Smulders heard about another theory—that the lines promote water runoff and aid adhesion, like treads on a tire. Smulders confirmed that pruney fingers have the advantage in wet conditions.

He's only just scratched the surface of how the wrinkles work. For now, though, his findings could boost the theory that a million years ago the ancestors of modern humans went through a semiaquatic state, when skin folds might have helped toes cling to slick rocks and fingers catch wriggling fish. —*Catherine Zuckerman*

Keen on Quinoa

Quinoa's reputation is blossoming. The seed of a goosefoot species that originated in Peru and Bolivia around Lake Titicaca, it's been a staple of Andean cuisine for millennia. Over the past decade other cultures have developed a taste for it too. Since 2007 U.S. imports have risen from 7 million to more than 70 million pounds a year.

This growing appetite is affecting South America. Farmers are struggling to meet demand, and some urban populations can't afford the resulting price increases. To cash in on the crop's popularity, countries on other continents have begun moving from consumer to cultivator. There are now quinoa farms in 56 countries, including France, Thailand, Australia, and the U.S. Quinoa is also being grown in Africa, where the UN hopes its high protein content will help fight hunger.

The long-term objective is diversity, says Kevin Murphy, a plant breeder at Washington State University. "There are hundreds of varieties of quinoa, and our goal is to develop the ideal one for different climates." For now most retail stores in the U.S. remain stocked with Andean quinoa. With continued crop experimentation, though, Murphy adds, it won't be long before locally grown—and less expensive— becomes an everyday option. —*Catherine Zuckerman*

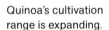
Quinoa's cultivation range is expanding.

Quinoa introduction
- Before 1975
- 1975-2000
- After 2000
- Native

Goosefoot (right) and its edible seeds (above)

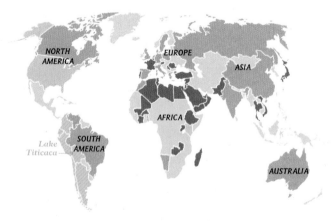

NORTH AMERICA

EUROPE

ASIA

AFRICA

Lake Titicaca

SOUTH AMERICA

AUSTRALIA

PHOTOS: MARK THIESSEN, NGM STAFF. NGM MAPS. SOURCE: DIDIER BAZILE, CIRAD, FRANCE

NEXT

The world's busiest air route connects Jeju and Seoul, South Korea. It saw 10.1 million passengers in 2012.

★ Seoul

Jeju

The discovery of this fossil helps explain the evolution of swifts and humming-birds in North America.

Early Bird

There's a new branch on the avian family tree. A 50-million-year-old fossilized bird found in Wyoming is thought to be an extinct cousin of modern hummingbirds and swifts. Based on the fossil's well-preserved plumage, paleontologist Daniel Ksepka believes *Eocypselus rowei*—four inches from head to tail—would have been a conventional flier. Its descendants' feathers specialized, growing long so swifts could stay aloft all day and short so hum-mingbirds could hover.
—*Catherine Zuckerman*

Face-to-Face Women have long been shown to be better than men at remem-bering faces. New research from Canada's McMaster University helps explain why. Kinesiologist Jennifer Heisz tracked the way men and women moved their eyes as they scanned pictures of faces (right). Both gen-ders started at the center and looked at the same features—eyes, nose, mouth—but wom-en made more eye movements between the features. "More frequent scanning generates a more vivid picture in your mind," says Heisz. Understanding how the brain memorizes vi-sual information could lead to improvements in how memory loss is treated. —*Daniel Stone*

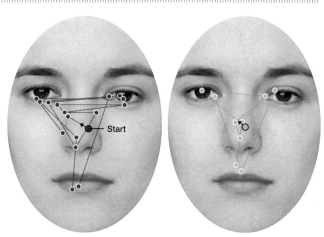

Start

EYE SPY Dots represent instances—observed over the course of five seconds—when each gender fixated on a facial feature.

Women ● 17
Men 10
0 seconds   1   2   3   4   5

PHOTO (TOP): JOHN WEINSTEIN, FIELD MUSEUM. SOURCE: LANCE GRANDE, *THE LOST WORLD OF FOSSIL LAKE*. PHOTO (BOTTOM): VISUAL DEVELOPMENT LAB, MCMASTER UNIVERSITY. GRAPHIC: MARGARET NG. ART (TOP): ÁLVARO VALIÑO. SOURCE: AMADEUS

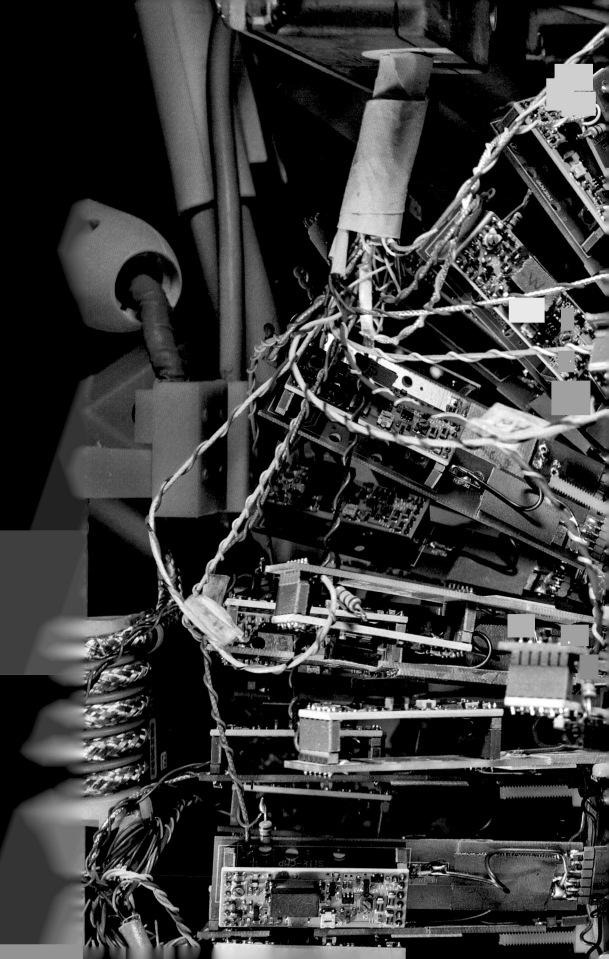

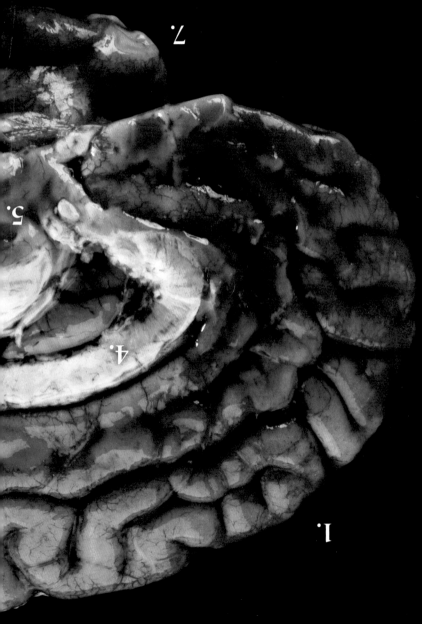

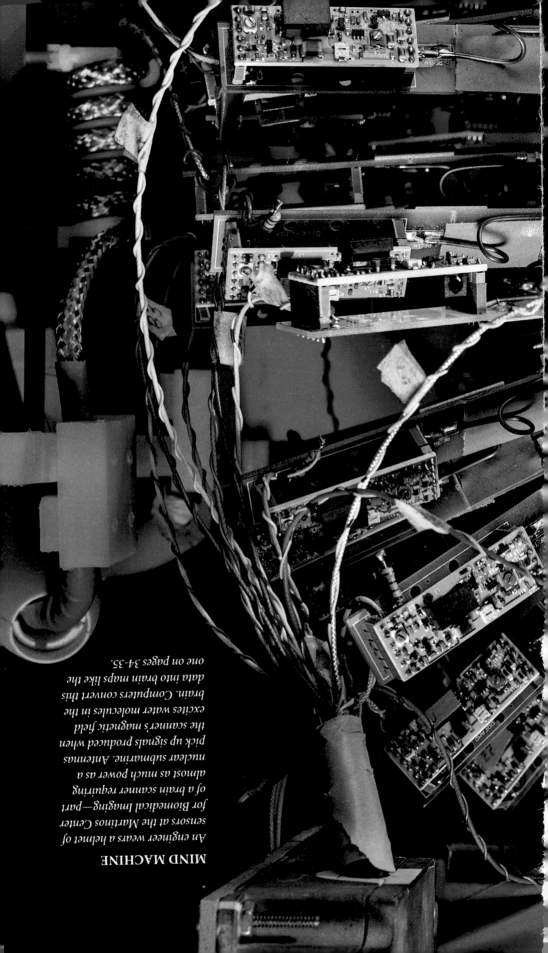

MIND MACHINE

An engineer wears a helmet of sensors at the Martinos Center for Biomedical Imaging—part of a brain scanner requiring almost as much power as a nuclear submarine. Antennas pick up signals produced when the scanner's magnetic field excites water molecules in the brain. Computers convert this data into brain maps like the one on pages 34-35.

SECRETS OF THE BRAIN

BRAIN

New technologies are shedding light on biology's greatest unsolved mystery: how the brain really works.

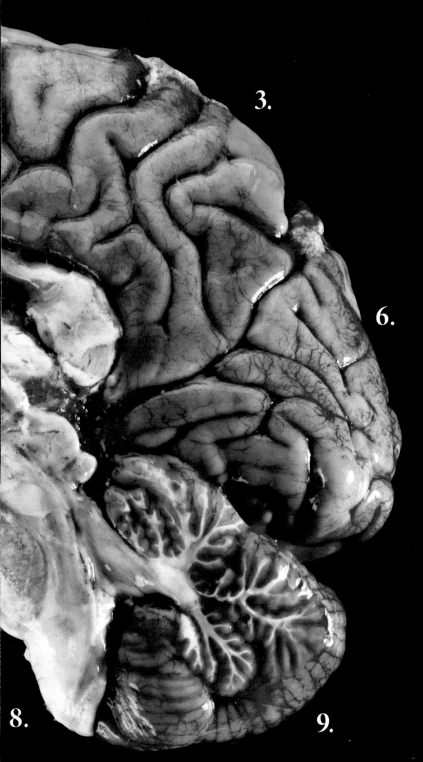

3.

6.

8.

9.

1. *Frontal cortex*
2. *Motor cortex*
3. *Parietal lobe*
4. *Corpus callosum*
5. *Thalamus*
6. *Occipital lobe*
7. *Temporal lobe*
8. *Brain stem*
9. *Cerebellum*

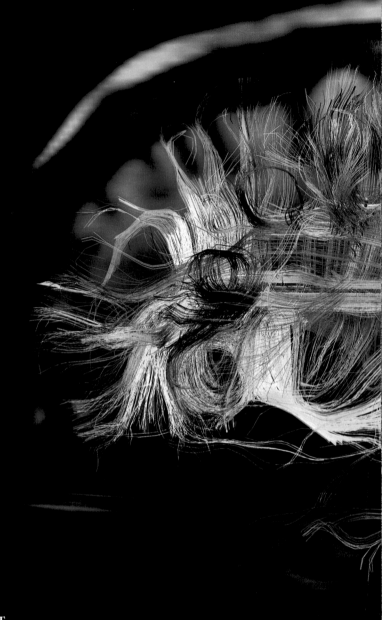

THE COLOR OF THOUGHT

The brain's many regions are connected by some 100,000 miles of fibers called white matter—enough to circle the Earth four times. Images like this, taken at the Martinos Center, reveal for the first time the specific pathways underlying cognitive functions. The pink and orange bundles, for example, transmit signals critical for language.

VAN WEDEEN AND L. L. WALD, MARTINOS CENTER
FOR BIOMEDICAL IMAGING, HUMAN CONNECTOME PROJECT

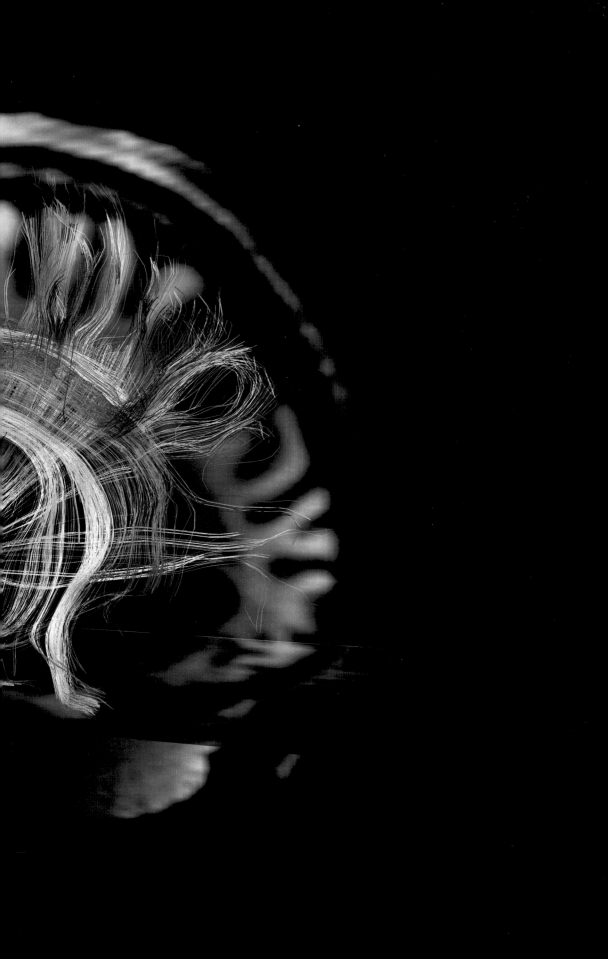

BY CARL ZIMMER
PHOTOGRAPHS BY ROBERT CLARK

Van Wedeen strokes his half-gray beard and leans toward his computer screen, scrolling through a cascade of files. We're sitting in a windowless library, surrounded by speckled boxes of old letters, curling issues of scientific journals, and an old slide projector that no one has gotten around to throwing out.

"It'll take me a moment to locate your brain," he says.

On a hard drive Wedeen has stored hundreds of brains—exquisitely detailed 3-D images from monkeys, rats, and humans, including me. Wedeen has offered to take me on a journey through my own head.

"We'll hit all the tourist spots," he promises, smiling.

This is my second trip to the Martinos Center for Biomedical Imaging, located in a former ship-rope factory on Boston Harbor. The first time, a few weeks ago, I offered myself as a neuroscientific guinea pig to Wedeen and his colleagues. In a scanning room I lay down on a slab, the back of my head resting in an open plastic box. A radiologist lowered a white plastic helmet over my face. I looked up at him through two eyeholes as he screwed the helmet tight, so that the 96 miniature antennas it contained

would be close enough to my brain to pick up the radio waves it was about to emit. As the slab glided into the cylindrical maw of the scanner, I thought of *The Man in the Iron Mask.*

The magnets that now surrounded me began to rumble and beep. For an hour I lay still, eyes closed, and tried to keep myself calm with my own thoughts. It wasn't easy. To squeeze as much resolution as possible out of the scanner, Wedeen and his colleagues had designed the device with barely enough room for a person of my build to fit inside. To tamp down the panic, I breathed smoothly and transported myself to places in my memory, at one point recalling how I had once walked my nine-year-old daughter to school through piles of blizzard snow.

As I lay there, I reflected on the fact that all of these thoughts and emotions were the creation of the three-pound loaf of flesh that was under scrutiny: my fear, carried by electrical impulses converging in an almond-shaped chunk of tissue in my brain called the amygdala, and the calming response to it, marshaled in regions of my frontal cortex. My memory of my walk with my daughter was coordinated by a seahorse-shaped fold of neurons called the hippocampus, which reactivated a vast web of links throughout my brain that had first fired when I had clambered over the snowbanks and formed those memories.

I was submitting to this procedure as part of my cross-country reporting to chronicle one of the great scientific revolutions of our times: the stunning advances in understanding the workings of the human brain. Some neuroscientists are zooming in on the fine structure of individual nerve cells, or neurons. Others are charting the biochemistry of the brain, surveying how our billions of neurons produce and employ thousands of different kinds of proteins. Still others, Wedeen among them, are creating in unprecedented detail representations of the brain's wiring: the network of some 100,000 miles of nerve fibers, called white matter, that connects the various components of the mind, giving rise to everything we think, feel, and perceive. The U.S. government is throwing its weight behind this research through the Brain Research

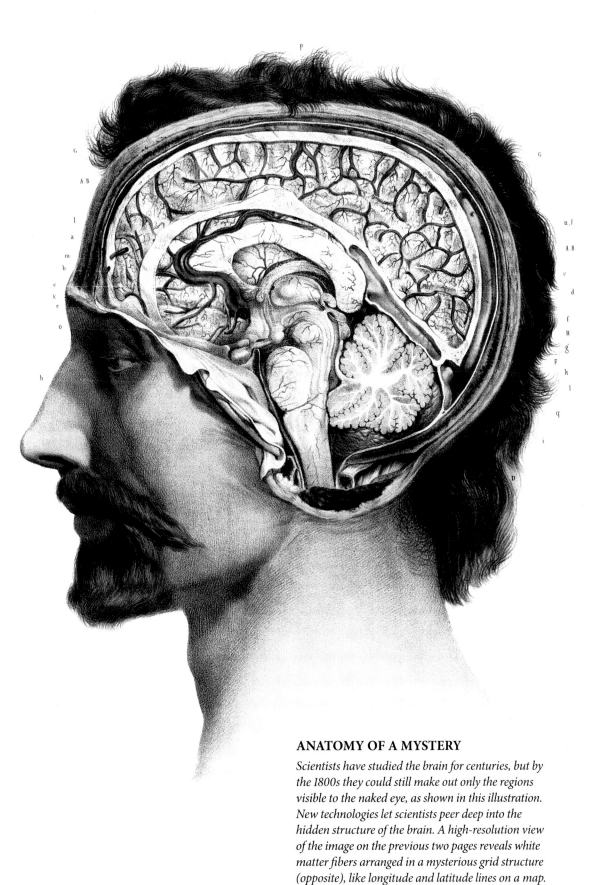

ANATOMY OF A MYSTERY

Scientists have studied the brain for centuries, but by the 1800s they could still make out only the regions visible to the naked eye, as shown in this illustration. New technologies let scientists peer deep into the hidden structure of the brain. A high-resolution view of the image on the previous two pages reveals white matter fibers arranged in a mysterious grid structure (opposite), like longitude and latitude lines on a map.

BURROWING DOWN TO SINGLE NERVE CELLS MAY FINALLY PROVIDE ANSWERS TO BASIC QUESTIONS ABOUT THE BRAIN.

through Advancing Innovative Neurotechnologies (BRAIN) Initiative. In an announcement last spring President Barack Obama said that the large-scale project aimed to speed up the mapping of our neural circuitry, "giving scientists the tools they need to get a dynamic picture of the brain in action."

As they see the brain in action, neuroscientists can also see its flaws. They are starting to identify differences in the structure of ordinary brains and brains of people with disorders such as schizophrenia, autism, and Alzheimer's disease. As they map the brain in greater detail, they may learn how to diagnose disorders by their effect on anatomy, and perhaps even understand how those disorders arise.

On my return trip to his lab Wedeen finally locates the image from my session in the scanner. My brain appears on his screen. His technique, called diffusion spectrum imaging, translates radio signals given off by the white matter into a high-resolution atlas of that neurological Internet. His scanner maps bundles of nerve fibers that form hundreds of thousands of pathways carrying information from one part of my brain to another. Wedeen paints each path a rainbow of colors, so that my brain appears as an explosion of colorful fur, like a psychedelic Persian cat.

Wedeen focuses in on particular pathways, showing me some of the circuitry important to language and other kinds of thought. Then he pares away most of the pathways in my brain, so that I can more easily see how they're organized. As he increases the magnification, something astonishing takes shape before me. In spite of the dizzying complexity of the circuits, they all intersect at right angles, like the lines on a sheet of graph paper.

"It's all grids," says Wedeen.

When Wedeen first unveiled the grid structure of the brain, in 2012, some scientists were skeptical, wondering if he'd uncovered only part of a much more tangled anatomy. But Wedeen

is more convinced than ever that the pattern is meaningful. Wherever he looks—in the brains of humans, monkeys, rats—he finds the grid. He notes that the earliest nervous systems in Cambrian worms were simple grids—just a pair of nerve cords running from head to tail, with runglike links between them. In our own lineage the nerves at the head end exploded into billions but still retained that gridlike structure. It's possible that our thoughts run like streetcars along these white matter tracks as signals travel from one region of the brain to another.

"There's zero chance that there are not principles lurking in this," says Wedeen, peering intently at the image of my brain. "We're just not yet in a position to see the simplicity."

SCIENTISTS ARE LEARNING so much about the brain now that it's easy to forget that for much of history we had no idea at all how it worked or even what it was. In the ancient world physicians believed that the brain was made of phlegm. Aristotle looked on it as a refrigerator, cooling off the fiery heart. From his time through the Renaissance, anatomists declared with great authority that our perceptions, emotions, reasoning, and actions were all the result of "animal spirits"—mysterious, unknowable vapors that swirled through cavities in our head and traveled through our bodies.

The scientific revolution in the 17th century began to change that. The British physician Thomas Willis recognized that the custardlike tissue of the brain was where our mental world existed. To understand how it worked, he dissected brains of sheep, dogs, and expired patients, producing the first accurate maps of the organ.

It would take another century for researchers to grasp that the brain is an electric organ. Instead of animal spirits, voltage spikes travel through it and out into the body's nervous system. Still, even in the 19th century scientists knew little about the paths those spikes followed. The Italian physician Camillo Golgi argued that the brain was a seamless connected web. Building on Golgi's research, the Spanish scientist Santiago Ramón y Cajal tested new ways of staining individual

Carl Zimmer wrote on bringing back extinct species in the April 2013 issue. Robert Clark's previous story, on sugar, was in the August 2013 issue.

neurons to trace their tangled branches. Cajal recognized what Golgi did not: that each neuron is a distinct cell, separate from every other one. A neuron sends signals down tendrils known as axons. A tiny gap separates the ends of axons from the receiving ends of neurons, called dendrites. Scientists would later discover that axons dump a cocktail of chemicals into the gap to trigger a signal in the neighboring neuron.

JEFF LICHTMAN, a neuroscientist, is the current Ramón y Cajal Professor of Arts and Sciences at Harvard, carrying Cajal's project into the 21st century. Instead of making pen-and-ink drawings of neurons stained by hand, he and his colleagues are creating extremely detailed three-dimensional images of neurons, revealing every bump and stalk branching from them. By burrowing down to the fine structure of individual nerve cells, they may finally get answers to some of the most basic questions about the nature of the brain. Each neuron has on average 10,000 synapses. Is there some order to their connections to other neurons, or are they random? Do they prefer linking to one type of neuron over others?

To produce the images, Lichtman and his colleagues load pieces of preserved mouse brain into a neuroanatomical version of a deli meat slicer, which pares off layers of tissue, each less than a thousandth the thickness of a strand of human hair. The scientists use an electron microscope to take a picture of each cross section, then use a computer to order them into a stack. Slowly a three-dimensional image takes shape—one that the scientists can explore as if they were in a submarine traveling through an underwater kelp forest.

"Everything is revealed," says Lichtman.

The only problem is the sheer enormity of "everything." So far the largest volume of a mouse's brain that Lichtman and his colleagues have managed to re-create is about the size of a grain of salt. Its data alone total a hundred terabytes, the amount of data in about 25,000 high-definition movies.

Once the scientists have gathered this information, the really hard work begins: looking

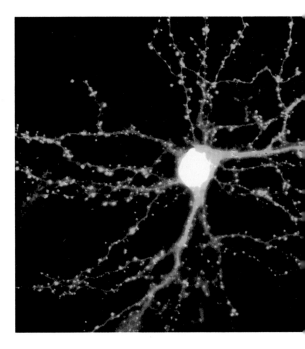

THE GLOW OF MEMORY

When you form a memory, "there's a physical change in the brain," says Don Arnold, of the University of Southern California. Red and green dots on the branches extending from this rat neuron show where it contacts other neurons. As the rat forms new memories, new dots appear and old ones vanish.

for the rules that organize the brain's seeming chaos. Recently Lichtman's postdoctoral researcher Narayanan Kasthuri set out to analyze every detail in a cylinder of mouse brain tissue measuring just a thousand cubic microns—a volume 1/100,000 the size of a grain of salt. He selected a region surrounding a short segment of a single axon, seeking to identify every neuron that passed through it.

That minuscule patch of brain turned out to be like a barrel of seething snakes. Kasthuri found a thousand axons and about 80 dendrites, each making about 600 connections with other neurons inside the cylinder. "It's a wake-up call to how much more complicated brains are than the way we think about them," says Lichtman.

JENNIFER ON THE BRAIN

Caltech and UCLA scientists use pictures of celebrities to study how the brain processes what the eyes see. In 2005 they found an individual nerve cell that fired only when subjects were shown pictures of Jennifer Aniston. Another neuron responded only to pictures of Halle Berry—even when she was masked as Catwoman. Follow-up studies suggest that relatively few neurons are involved in representing any given person, place, or concept, making the brain staggeringly efficient at storing information.

IMAGE CREDITS AT *NGM COM/BRAIN*

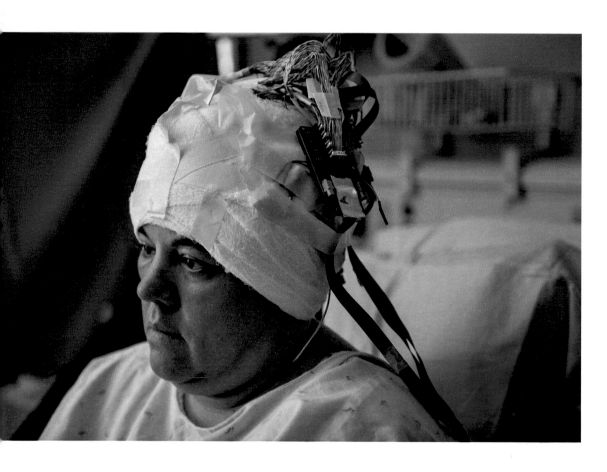

LISTENING IN

How did scientists discover the "Jennifer Aniston neuron"? At UCLA's Medical Center for Neuroscience electrodes are implanted in the brains of epileptic patients such as Crystal Hawkins. The next time she has a seizure, the electrodes will pinpoint its source, allowing neurosurgeons to target what brain tissue to remove. The electrodes also provide a rare opportunity to eavesdrop on neurons functioning normally, which led to the discovery of nerve cells that respond to specific faces.

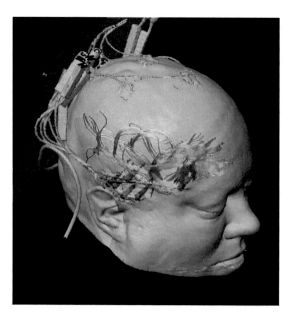

THE SECRET TO MANY DISEASES MAY BE HIDING IN THE BRAIN'S GENES, AS THEY SHUT DOWN OR SWITCH ON ABNORMALLY.

Complicated, but not random. Lichtman and Kasthuri discovered that every neuron made nearly all its connections with just one other one, scrupulously avoiding a connection with almost all the other neurons packed tightly around it. "They seem to care who they're connected to," Lichtman says.

Lichtman can't say yet whether this fastidious pattern is a general rule or a feature of just the tiny area of mouse brain he sampled. Even as they scale up the technology, he and his colleagues will need another two years to complete a scan of all 70 million neurons in a mouse. I ask about scanning an entire human brain, which contains a thousand times more neurons than a mouse's.

"I don't dwell on that," he says, with a laugh. "It's too painful."

WHEN AND IF LICHTMAN completes his three-dimensional portrait of the brain, it will reveal much—but it will still be only an exquisitely detailed sculpture. His imaged neurons are hollow models; real neurons are crammed with living DNA, proteins, and other molecules. Each type of neuron uses a distinct set of genes to build the molecular machinery it needs to do its own job. Light-sensitive neurons in the eyes produce photon-catching proteins, for example, and neurons in a region called the substantia nigra produce a protein called dopamine, crucial to our sense of reward. The geography of proteins is essential to understanding how the brain works— and how it goes awry. In Parkinson's disease the substantia nigra neurons produce less dopamine than normal, for reasons that aren't yet clear. Alzheimer's disease scatters tangles of protein through the brain, although scientists have yet to firmly settle on how those tangles give rise to the devastating dementia the disease causes.

A map of the brain's molecular machinery called the Allen Brain Atlas has been generated at the Allen Institute for Brain Science in Seattle, founded ten years ago with funds from Microsoft co-founder Paul Allen. Using the brains of recently deceased people, donated by their families, researchers there use a high-resolution magnetic resonance imaging (MRI) scan of each

brain as a three-dimensional road map, then slice it into microscopically thin sections that are mounted on glass slides. They then douse the sections with chemicals that reveal the presence of active genes harbored in the neurons.

So far the researchers have mapped the brains of six people, charting the activity of 20,000 protein-coding genes at 700 sites within each brain. It's a colossal amount of data, and they've only begun to make sense of it. The scientists estimate that 84 percent of all the genes in our DNA become active somewhere in the adult brain. (A simpler organ like the heart or pancreas requires far fewer genes to work.) In each of the 700 sites the scientists studied, the neurons switch on a distinct collection of genes. In a preliminary survey of two regions of the brain, the scientists compared a thousand genes that were already known to be important for neuron function. From one person to the next, the areas of the brain where each of those genes was active were practically identical. It looks as if the brain has a finely grained genetic landscape, with special combinations of genes carrying out tasks in different locations. The secret to many diseases of the brain may be hiding in that landscape, as certain genes shut down or switch on abnormally.

All the information from the Allen Brain Atlas is posted online, where other scientists can navigate through the data with custom-made software. Already they're making new discoveries. A team of Brazilian scientists, for instance, has used it to study a devastating brain disorder called Fahr's disease, which calcifies regions deep inside the brain, leading to dementia. Some cases of Fahr's disease had already been linked to a mutation in the gene *SLC20A2*. In the atlas the scientists found that *SLC20A2* is most active in precisely the regions that are targeted by the disease. They also found a network of other genes that is most active in the same areas, and now they're trying to find out whether they're involved in Fahr's disease as well.

OF ALL THE NEW WAYS of visualizing the brain, perhaps the most remarkable is one invented by Stanford neuroscientist and psychiatrist

INTIMATE VIEW

Two hundred sections of a piece of mouse brain, each less than 1/1,000 the thickness of a human hair, are readied to be imaged by an electron microscope. Arranged in stacks, 10,000 such photomicrographs form a 3-D model no larger than a grain of salt (in tweezers). A human brain visualized at this level of detail would require an amount of data equal to all the written material in all the libraries of the world.

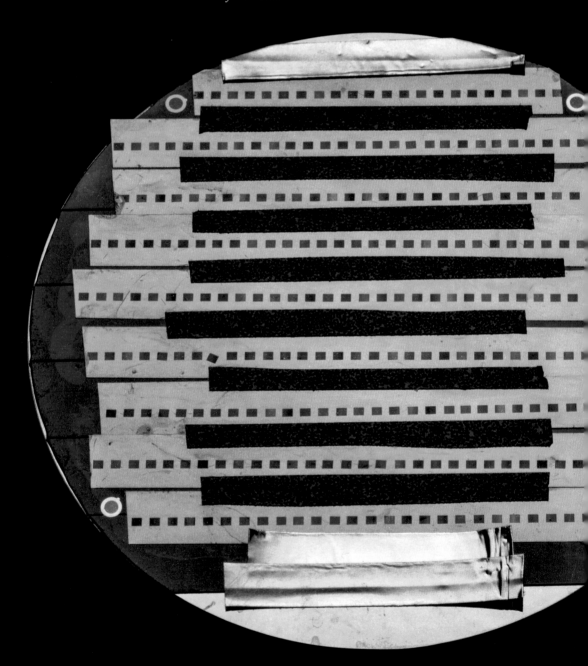

A VOYAGE INTO THE
BRAIN

*Thought, feeling, sense, action—all derive
from unimaginably complex interactions among
billions of nerve cells. A section of mouse
brain (above) no larger than a grain of salt
serves as a window into this
hidden world.*

ANATOMY OF A NERVE CELL

Cell body
The neuron's power-
house, responsible for
generating energy and
synthesizing proteins

An image a millimeter
high—less than four-
hundredths of an
inch—shows nerve cells
arranged in orderly
layers and columns.

*The 1-mm image is from
a different data set than
the other images.

1 mm = 1,000 microns*

100 microns

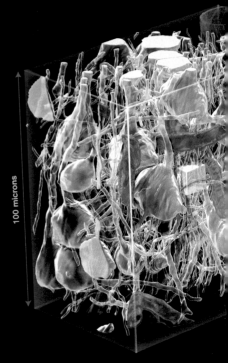

DEEP BRAIN DIVE

For the first time scientists can visualize how
neurons actually connect with one another.
The three blocks at right have been colorized
but are not an artist's conception: They show,
at increasing levels of magnification, real
neurons in part of a mouse's brain receiving
signals from the face. Technology may soon
make possible a similar reconstruction of an
entire mouse brain—and eventually of the
vastly more complicated architecture of the
human brain, opening the way for advances
in understanding schizophrenia, depression,
and other mental diseases.

A section a hundredth the size
reveals blood vessels among
pink cell bodies and a tangle
of their axons and dendrites.

HALF THE WORLD'S HARD DRIVES
Visualizing neurons at the level of
detail shown in these images requires
unprecedented computing power.
Producing an image of an entire
human brain at the same resolution
would consume nearly half the world's
current digital storage capacity.

Storage capacity
needed to produce
mouse brain image
450,000 terabytes

Storage capacity
needed to produce
human brain image
1.3 billion terabytes

Global digital
storage, 2012:
2.7 billion terabytes

JASON TREAT AND KURT MUTCHLER, NGM STAFF, ANTHONY SCHICK. ART: BRYAN CHRISTIE
PHOTO (FLAP): JOSH L. MORGAN, HARVARD UNIVERSITY; ARTHUR WETZEL, PITTSBURGH SUPERCOMPUTING CENTER

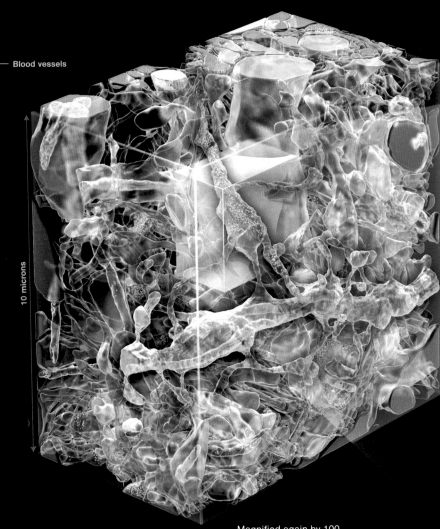

Dendrites
Branching projections
that pick up signals
from other neurons

Blood vessels

10 microns

Magnified again by 100,
this section more clearly
shows axons (blue) and
dendrites (yellow). Budlike
dendritic spines receive
information from other
cells' axons across gaps
called synapses.

SOURCES: JEFF LICHTMAN, HARVARD UNIVERSITY; DANIEL BERGER, MASSACHUSETTS INSTITUTE OF TECHNOLOGY; INTERNATIONAL DATA CORPORATION

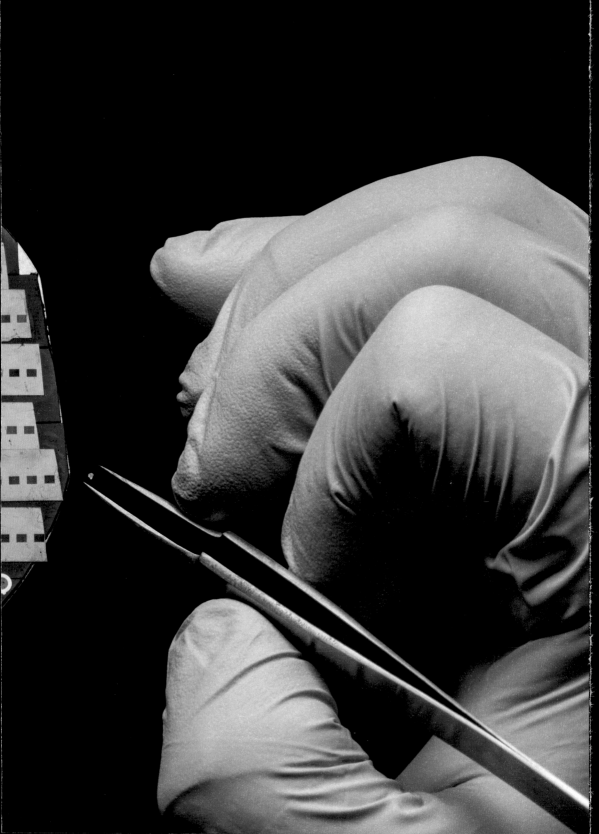

Axon
A long nerve fiber that conducts information from the cell body in the form of an electrical impulse

Axonal terminal
End point of an axon's branches, where electrical impulses are discharged; releases neurotransmitters that carry chemical messages to other cells' dendrites

Glial cells
The glue of the nervous system, supporting, feeding, and protecting neurons

1 micron

Magnified yet again, this section reveals synaptic vesicles (yellow grains) containing neurotransmitters, which carry chemical messages across synapses, signaling the receiving nerve cell to fire or stop firing.

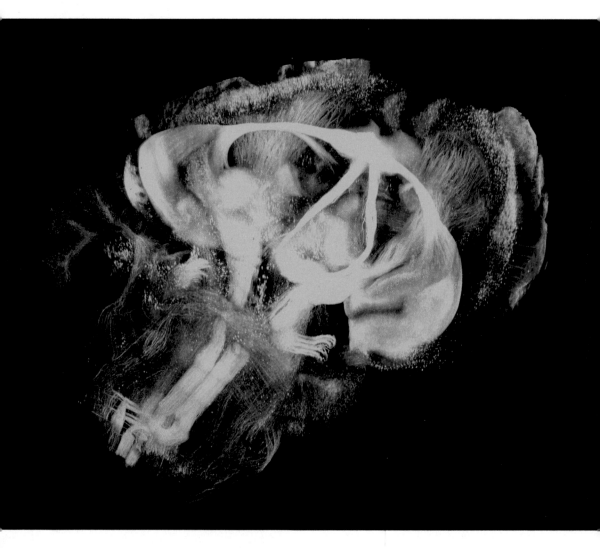

The brain is a world consisting of a number of unexplored continents and great stretches of unknown territory.

The brain is a world consisting of a number of unexplored continents and great stretches of unknown territory.

A CLEAR VIEW

Scientists at Stanford University bathe a mouse brain (far left) in chemicals that remove fats and other molecules, rendering it transparent (left). Proteins can then be added that bind only to certain neurons. Below, a green-glowing protein reveals the ubiquity of a type of neuron that accounts for just one percent of a mouse's brain.

TO SEE THE BRAIN, SCIENTISTS AT STANFORD UNIVERSITY BEGIN BY MAKING IT AS TRANSPARENT AS A GLASS MARBLE.

Karl Deisseroth and his colleagues. To see the brain, they begin by making it disappear.

On my visit to Deisseroth's lab, undergraduate Jenelle Wallace led me to a bench where half a dozen beakers rested in a plastic-foam base. She pulled one out and pointed to a grape-size mouse brain resting at the bottom. I didn't look at the brain so much as through it. It was nearly as transparent as a glass marble.

Needless to say, a normal human or mouse brain is decidedly opaque, its cells swathed in fat and other compounds that block light. That's why Cajal had to dye neurons in order to see them and why Lichtman's group and the Allen Institute scientists slice the brain into thin sections to gain access to its inner depths. The advantage of a transparent brain is that it allows us to peer into its workings while the organ is still intact. Along with postdoctoral researcher Kwanghun Chung, Deisseroth came up with a recipe to replace the light-scattering compounds in the brain with transparent molecules. After making a mouse brain transparent in this way, they can then douse the brain with glowing chemical labels that latch on to only certain proteins or trace a specific pathway connecting neurons in distant regions of the brain. The scientists can then wash out one set of chemicals and add another that reveals the location and structure of a different type of neuron—in effect untangling the Gordian knot of neural circuits one by one. "You don't have to take it apart to show the wiring," says Deisseroth.

It's not easy to dazzle neuroscientists, but Deisseroth's method, dubbed CLARITY, has left his colleagues awestruck. "It's pretty badass," says Christof Koch, the chief scientific officer at the Allen Institute. Wedeen has called the research "spectacular…unlike anything else in the field."

Because of our shared evolutionary heritage, a clarified mouse brain can reveal a great deal about human brain function. But Deisseroth's ultimate goal is to perform the same transformation with a human brain—a far more difficult

For more on the mind, tune in to the third season of *Brain Games*, premiering in January on the National Geographic Channel. Check local listings.

task, not least because a human brain is 3,000 times as large as that of a mouse.

A CLARITY picture showing the location of just one type of protein in just one human brain would create a monstrous heap of data—about two petabytes, or the equivalent of several hundred thousand high-def movies. Deisseroth anticipates that CLARITY may someday help the sort of people he treats in his psychiatric practice, by revealing hidden features of disorders like autism and depression. But for now he's keeping those hopes in check.

"We have so far to go before we can affect treatments that I tell people, Don't even think about that yet," he says. "It's just a voyage of discovery for now."

AS REVEALING AS A transparent brain may prove to be, it will still be dead. Scientists need different tools to explore the terrain of living brains. The scanners Wedeen uses to trace white matter patterns can, with different programming, record the brain in action. Functional magnetic resonance imaging (fMRI) pinpoints regions of the brain recruited during a mental task. Over the past couple of decades fMRI has helped reveal networks involved in all manner of thought processes, from recognizing faces to enjoying a cup of coffee to remembering a traumatic event.

It's easy to be dazzled by fMRI images, which festoon the brain with rainbow blobs. But it's important to bear in mind that those images are actually quite coarse. The most powerful scanners can record activity only down to the scale of a cubic millimeter—a sesame seed's worth of tissue. Within that space, hundreds of thousands of neurons are firing in synchronized patterns, trading signals. How those signals give rise to the larger patterns revealed by fMRI remains mysterious.

"There are ridiculously simple questions about the cortex that we can't answer at all," says Clay Reid, a former colleague of Jeff Lichtman's at Harvard who moved to the Allen Institute in 2012.

Reid has come to Seattle hoping to answer some of those questions with a grand series of experiments he and his colleagues call Mind-Scope. Their goal is to understand how a large

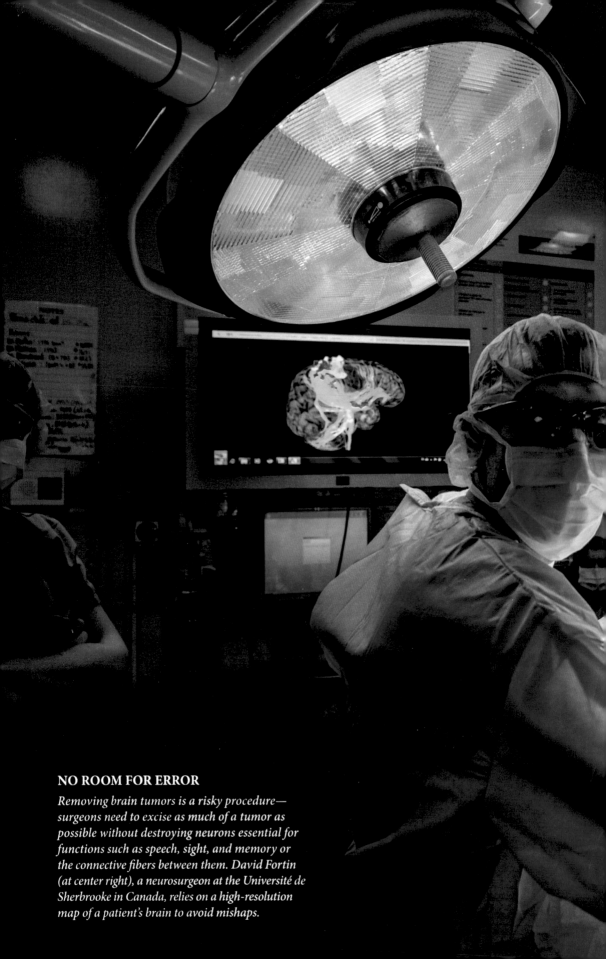

NO ROOM FOR ERROR

*Removing brain tumors is a risky procedure—
surgeons need to excise as much of a tumor as
possible without destroying neurons essential for
functions such as speech, sight, and memory or
the connective fibers between them. David Fortin
(at center right), a neurosurgeon at the Université de
Sherbrooke in Canada, relies on a high-resolution
map of a patient's brain to avoid mishaps.*

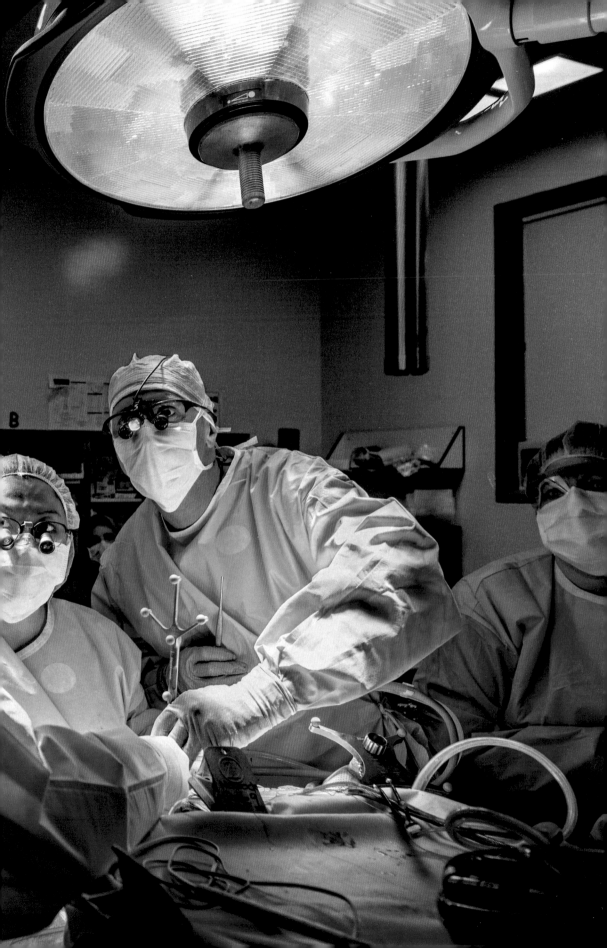

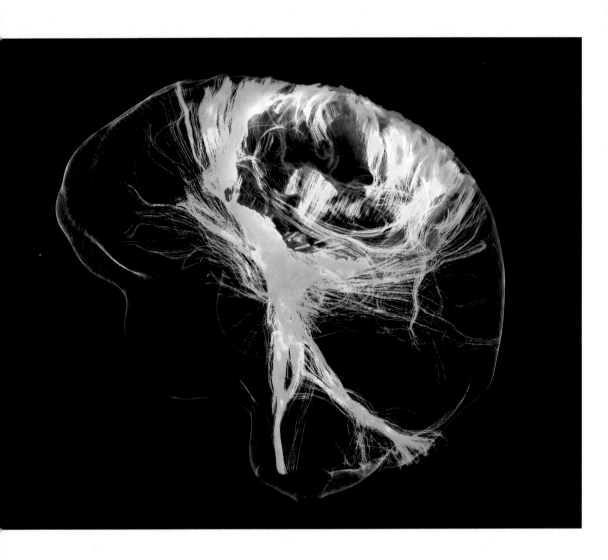

A GUIDED HAND

Scans of one of Fortin's patients revealed that a tumor (red, above) had grown into a region controlling the movement of hands and feet. As he removed parts of the tumor (left), Fortin applied current to the region to determine if neighboring neurons were critical for movement. "There was a lot of motor function still active in this patient," says Maxime Descoteaux, one of the Université de Sherbrooke scientists who made the brain scan. "So the surgeon in this case was more conservative than aggressive."

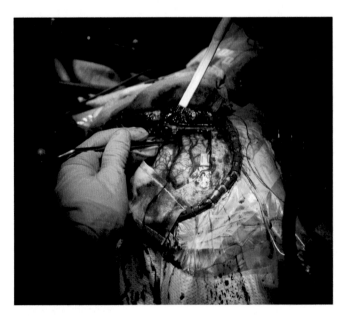

 MAXIME DESCOTEAUX AND MAXIME CHAMBERLAND, SHERBROOKE CONNECTIVITY IMAGING LAB, UNIVERSITÉ DE SHERBROOKE (TOP)

IF THEIR MODELS ARE ACCURATE, THE RESEARCHERS WILL BE ABLE TO LITERALLY READ THE MIND OF A MOUSE.

number of neurons carry out a complex task.

The function Reid and his colleagues have chosen to decipher is vision. Scientists have been investigating how we see for decades, but they've been able to study it only piecemeal. A neuroscientist might place an electrode in the region of a mouse's brain involved in visual perception and then note whether nearby neurons fire when the animal sees a particular image.

This approach has allowed scientists to map regions of the visual brain that specialize in different tasks, such as detecting the edges of an object or perceiving brightness. But scientists haven't been able to see all those regions work together at once—to learn how the million or so neurons in the visual regions of a mouse's brain instantly put information together into the image of a cat.

Reid and his colleagues are setting out to solve that problem by engineering mice so that their visual neurons will release flashes of light when they fire. The flashes record the neural activity when a mouse sees a specific object, be it a cat, a snake, or an appealing piece of cheese. The scientists can then compile the data to create massive mathematical models of vision. If the models are accurate, the researchers will be able to literally read the mind of a mouse.

"Our goal is to reconstruct what the mouse sees," says Reid. "And I think we can do it."

REID'S RESEARCH on mouse vision is another step toward neuroscience's ultimate goal: a comprehensive view of how this vastly complicated organ really works—what the scientists I talked to call a theory of the brain. Such a grand vision is still a long way off, and for the most part, the search for it has yet to change the way doctors treat patients. But there is one line of research—brain-machine interfaces—where the mapping of the mind has started to change people's lives.

When she was 43 years old, Cathy Hutchinson suffered a massive stroke, leaving her unable to move or speak. Lying in her bed in Massachusetts General Hospital, she gradually figured out that her doctors didn't know if she was brain-dead or still aware. Her sister asked Hutchinson

if she could understand her. She managed to answer by moving her eyes up on command.

"It gave me such a relief," Hutchinson tells me 17 years later, "because everybody talked about me as if I was dying."

It is a chilly winter day at her home in eastern Massachusetts, and she's sitting in a wheelchair in the middle of the living room, dressed in a dark green jogging suit and sneakers. Still almost completely paralyzed and unable to speak, she communicates by looking at letters arrayed on a computer monitor bolted to her wheelchair, a camera tracking the movement of a tiny metal disk attached to the center of her eyeglasses.

Near the top of the brain is a region called the motor cortex, where we generate commands to move our muscles. For more than a century we've known that each part of the cortex corresponds to a particular area of the body. When people like Hutchinson become paralyzed, the motor cortex often remains intact, but it can't communicate with the rest of the body, because its connections have been destroyed. John Donoghue, a neuroscientist at Brown University, wanted to find a way to help people with paralysis by tapping into the signals from their motor cortex. Perhaps they could eventually learn to type on a computer or operate a machine merely with their thoughts. Donoghue spent years developing an implant and testing the device on monkeys. Once he and his colleagues knew it was safe, they were ready to start working with human patients.

One of them was Hutchinson. In 2005 surgeons at Rhode Island Hospital drilled a hole the size of a poker chip in her skull and inserted the sensor for Donoghue's device. About the size of a ladybug, the sensor contained a hundred miniature needles, which, pressing into Hutchinson's motor cortex, recorded the signals from nearby neurons. A set of wires anchored to this device passed through the hole in her skull and led to a metal connector sitting on her scalp.

After her surgery had healed, the Brown University researchers plugged Hutchinson's implant into a cable that relayed signal patterns from her brain to a cart of computers they wheeled into her room. As a first step, the scientists trained

BY THOUGHT ALONE

A rhesus macaque walks with the aid of a pneumatically powered exoskeleton controlled by a computer reading signals from electrodes implanted in the monkey's motor cortex. Miguel Nicolelis and colleagues at Duke University are developing similar devices that could allow paralyzed humans to walk again.

the computers to recognize signals in her motor cortex and use them to move a computer cursor around a screen. This was achieved the first time she tried because they had learned how to translate patterns of brain activity into movements. Two years later they coupled a robotic arm to the computers, refining a program that could interpret Hutchinson's brain signals to move the arm forward and back, to raise it up and down, and to open its robotic fingers and squeeze them shut.

After just a few sessions Hutchinson, the computer, and the robotic arm had become a team. "It felt natural," she tells me. So natural that one day she reached out for a cinnamon latte, grabbed it, and brought it to her lips to drink.

"Cathy's smile when she put down that drink—that's everything," Donoghue says.

Today Donoghue and other scientists are building on that success, hoping to create human-machine interfaces that will be powerful, safe, and easy. At Duke University Miguel Nicolelis has been experimenting with exoskeletons that strap on to the body. Signals from the brain control each limb. Already he has gotten monkeys to control full-body exoskeletons. If all goes well, a paraplegic wearing a simpler version of the device will deliver the opening kick at the 2014 World Cup in Nicolelis's native Brazil.

"Eventually brain implants will become as common as heart implants," says Nicolelis. "I have no doubt about that."

When it comes to the brain, predicting the future is a tricky game. Advances in the past have inspired giddy expectations that in many cases have not been met. "We can't tell a schizophrenic brain from an autistic brain from a normal brain," says Christof Koch. But the research that's going on now, he believes, is moving neuroscience to a remarkable new stage. "I think we can begin to put the pieces together." □

BIONIC BRAIN

People with spinal cord injuries can't move because the brain and body no longer communicate. Scientists hope to restore motion with a mechanical skeleton controlled by the wearer's thoughts. It's a daunting challenge: Hundreds of sensors must be implanted in the brain to send commands to the exoskeleton. Signals must also travel in reverse, from touch sensors telling the brain where the body is in space.

Electrodes the width of a human hair are arranged in arrays like bristles in a toothbrush. Experiments on monkeys (opposite page) use four arrays to monitor 2,000 neurons. Many more would be needed for a human to walk.

1 Multiple electrode arrays send signals to a central processing unit in a helmet, which compiles signals into coherent commands.

2 Commands are transmitted wirelessly to a backpack computer that coordinates the complex motions needed to walk.

3 Tiny motors on the exoskeleton pick up computer commands to move joints and limbs.

4 Touch sensors provide feedback from the environment.

To sense where the body is in space, the exoskeleton is dotted with sensors that pick up texture, movement, and pressure through a plastic covering, much like a touch screen. These signals are transmitted back to the brain.

JASON TREAT, NGM STAFF; ANTHONY SCHICK
ART: BRYAN CHRISTIE
SOURCES: MIGUEL NICOLELIS, DUKE UNIVERSITY; GORDON CHENG, INSTITUTE FOR COGNITIVE SYSTEMS, TECHNISCHE UNIVERSITÄT MÜNCHEN, GERMANY

Now and then it's good to drive out west
of Minneapolis and look around and see
where you are. On the prairie, I stand by
my car on a gravel road that goes west to
the end of the world. It's sheer grandeur:
vast, silent, like the mind of God, and
I'm an insect with a vehicle.

There's No Place Like Home

A Personal Geography by Garrison Keillor

Photographs by Erika Larsen

My grandma Dora Keillor was riding in my dad's car one winter day in 1957 when the car spun out of control on an icy highway. Grandma didn't cry out. John, she said, "Which way is north?" I share that need for clarity.

Olivia Rowe is my aunt Josephine's great-granddaughter. Her level gaze and dark hair remind me of Aunt Jo, who was a gardener and kept a flock of chickens. Olivia keeps pigeons, 14 of them. This one is named Angel.

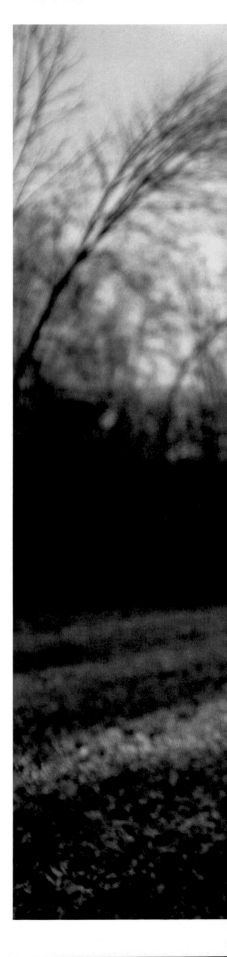

An old bus, restored, like the one
I rode back and forth to the U.
I dearly loved school, and the sight
of a bus cheers me up—if it
stopped, and I boarded it, I might
be 22 again and on my way to
Allen Tate's poetry seminar.

A graceful tower named for a crooked financier, where schoolchildren on field trips in the early fifties stood on the observation deck on the 31st floor and saw all of Minneapolis, beyond the streetcar lines to the outlying farms.

My parents' house, painted on a slice of wood by their friend Mr. Walton in Orlando, Florida, who did a nice job with the snow.

A pproaching Minneapolis-St. Paul Airport from the east, the plane descends over the green fields of Wisconsin and the St. Croix River into Minnesota, just above the farm in Denmark Township where my mother spent happy summer days visiting her sister Margaret—snapshots of girls in white summer dresses standing, holding their bicycles, Grace and Elsie and Ina squinting in the bright 1934 sunlight—and passes south of downtown St. Paul and the gleam of steel rails that carried Dad in the mail car of the *Empire Builder* departing Union Depot for Seattle, a .38 snub-nosed revolver on his hip, and past the cathedral near

where I now live on a street of old stone mausoleums and the hospital where I walked in one day and said, "I think I'm having a stroke" (and I was), and we bank over Mendota, where back in my drinking days I hung out in a club devoted to New Orleans jazz and heard the great Billie and DeDe Pierce, and Willie and Percy Humphrey, and we come in low over the Minnesota River and as the plane touches down on the runway, I can see the hill where I used to park in a car with a girl and watch planes land and also make out, back in the days of the front seat when two people could get involved with each other in thrilling ways. A one-minute flight into the past, and if we'd landed from the north, there'd be more.

THERE'S A NEWER north-south runway, and on that approach I don't recognize a thing. It's all road tangle and malls, small and large, and we descend below 5,000 feet, and still I can't get my bearings—it could be the outskirts of Dallas or Tangier—and I start to feel I've lost my place in the world. I was born here. I'm 71 years old. I've lived most of my life here. I refuse to use a GPS here. And it is distressing to come home and not know where I am. But driving east from the airport, there is the Mississippi, and I am reoriented.

My grandma Dora Keillor was riding in my dad's car one winter day in 1957 when the car spun out of control on an icy highway and did a doughnut or two and stopped, still on the road. Grandma didn't cry out; she looked straight ahead out the windshield. "John," she said, "which way is north?" I share that need for clarity. When a man has lived in one place so long, he takes comfort in landmarks. The State Theater, the Basilica of St. Mary, the Grain Belt beer sign on Hennepin. I will go out of my way to cruise by the white tower of the horticulture building at the state fairgrounds and the grandstand and the remains of the racetrack where auto thrill-show drivers raced late-model Fords off ramps and through flaming hoops and a woman in a spangly suit dived from a high tower into a water tank. When Northwestern National Bank was sold to a giant chain, whose brass decided to do away with the beloved Weatherball ("When the Weatherball is white, colder weather is in sight"), it was like a death in the family.

The geography of Minneapolis-St. Paul is simple: Two interlocking cities—the Great River with its rhythmic spelling *M-i-ss-i-ss-i-pp-i* flowing in from the north, through Anoka and over St. Anthony Falls, past the glass towers of downtown Minneapolis crowded around the Foshay

Tower, the brave little skyscraper of my childhood, and the university campus with its long leafy mall and stone columns with the inscription about men being ennobled by understanding, which we certainly hope will come true someday, and the very noble Franklin Avenue bridge, and Fort Snelling, where, starting in 1819, our predecessors brought whiskey and smallpox to the frontier and where, in 1861, the First Minnesota Volunteers mustered and later took horrible casualties at Gettysburg but held their ground. Where the Minnesota River joins it from the west, the Mississippi does a sideways S through St. Paul, its rail yards, University Avenue with its entrepreneurial churn of storefront start-ups, Asian restaurants, muffler shops, then it crosses town near the great dome of the capitol with the team of golden horses on the roof, and bends south toward Red Wing, Winona, Dubuque, down to Prof. Harold Hill and Huck Finn territory. The cities contain stately lakes—Como and Phalen in St. Paul; in Minneapolis, Nokomis, Hiawatha, Harriet, Calhoun, Cedar, and Lake of the Isles, pools of ease and elegance on the asphalt grid—and Lake Minnetonka, the prairie Riviera, off to the southwest.

This geography was imprinted in my brain back when I learned my alphabet from the avenues of Minneapolis (Aldrich, Bryant, Colfax, Dupont, Emerson, Fremont, Girard, Humboldt, Irving, James, Knox through Xerxes, York, and Zenith), which I might recite on my deathbed to prove I still have brain function. Superimposed over that geography, like a Jackson Pollock painted on a fishnet, is the geography of a man's life, the griefs and pleasures of various streets, Washington Avenue along which I had to memorize a Bible verse every Sunday, Nicollet and the funeral home and the corpse in the coffin, street corners where I used to wait for a bus on those killer mornings in January and February, the landmarks of experience—Loring Park, where I liked to sit and smoke after a ten-hour day in the hotel scullery where I washed pots and pans after high school. At the end of a day in the steam of the dishwasher, a summer evening was blessedly cool, and the smoke was ecstatic. Girls strolled by in loose white blouses and skirts, and some stopped and asked for a light and leaned down, holding their hair back, and the lit match illuminated their faces like medieval saints. In that park I am still 18 and in a state of adoration, but driving east on Franklin I feel an ache in my gut passing the building where I helped clean the small dim apartment of my former wife after she died, her souvenirs scattered around, the loneliness of the furniture, the unspeakable sadness of the cupboards full of health food. I drove to the river and sat by the bridge and wept 30 years' worth of tears.

My Minneapolis is the south side: Blocks of stucco bungalows under majestic archways of elms, small well-kept yards, the birdbath, gazing globe, coiled green rubber hose, grape arbor, steel barrel incinerator, and skinny frame garage on the alley where my mother grew up around 38th Street with her 12 siblings, most of whom settled in the neighborhood. And if I walk those blocks today, I feel the old claustrophobia of Sunday afternoon after dinner, the smell of wax and polish, the figurines on the walnut highboy, the good china in glass cabinets, Grandpa and Grandma on the sofa, nibbling on butterscotch caramel candy, George Beverly Shea singing "How Great Thou Art." We attended church at the Grace & Truth Gospel Hall on 14th Avenue South, where a preacher clutched his suspenders and spoke glowingly of Eternity, and I grew up one of the Brethren, the Chosen to whom God had vouchsafed the Knowledge of All Things that was denied to the great and mighty. The Second Coming was imminent, we would rise to the sky. We walked around Minneapolis carefully, wary of television, dance music, tobacco, baubles, bangles, flashy cars, liquor, the theater, the modern novel—all of them tempting us away from the singular life that Jesus commanded us to lead.

In 1947 Dad got a GI loan and built us a little white house north of the city on an acre of

The Keillor Reader, *a collection of stories and essays, will be published by Viking in May. Erika Larsen's photographs of Sami reindeer herders in Scandinavia appeared in the November 2011 issue.*

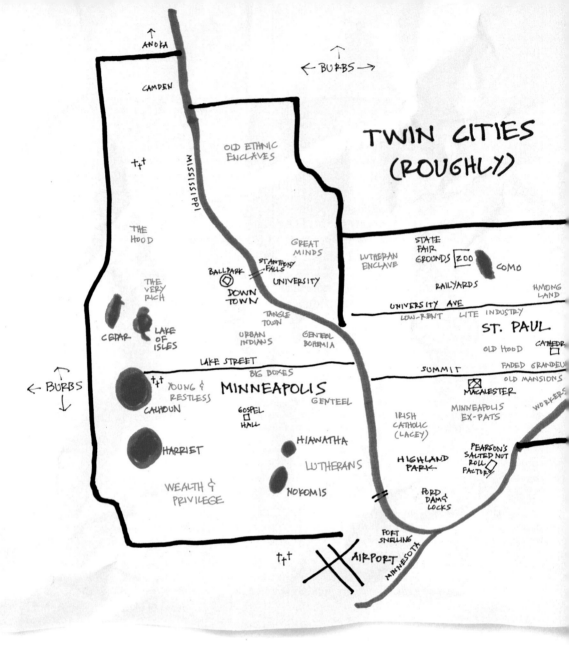

TWIN CITIES (ROUGHLY)

Map labels:

ANOKA

← BURBS →

CAMDEN

OLD ETHNIC ENCLAVES

MISSISSIPPI

THE HOOD

GREAT MINDS

STATE FAIR GROUNDS ZOO

COMO

LUTHERAN ENCLAVE

RAILYARDS

HMONG LAND

BALLPARK

ST. ANTHONY FALLS

UNIVERSITY

DOWN TOWN

UNIVERSITY AVE

LOW-RENT   LITE INDUSTRY

ST. PAUL

THE VERY RICH

TANGLE TOWN

CEDAR

LAKE OF ISLES

URBAN INDIANS

GENTEEL BOHEMIA

OLD HOOD   CATHEDR.

FADED GRANDEUR

LAKE STREET

BIG BOXES

SUMMIT

OLD MANSIONS

← BURBS ↓

YOUNG & RESTLESS

MINNEAPOLIS

MACALESTER

WORKERS

GENTEEL

MINNEAPOLIS EX-PATS

CALHOUN

GOSPEL HALL

IRISH CATHOLIC (LACEY)

HARRIET

HIAWATHA

PEARSON'S SALTED NUT ROLL FACTORY

LUTHERANS

HIGHLAND PARK

WEALTH & PRIVILEGE

NOKOMIS

FORD DAMS & LOCKS

FORT SNELLING

AIRPORT

MINNESOTA

cornfield in Brooklyn Township, a stone's throw from the Mississippi, so he could have a garden, farm boy that he was. He loved fresh vegetables, sweet corn and tomatoes and strawberries. A half-acre garden was a lot of work, but he had six kids, and he felt that work was a privilege, and he wanted us to grow up privileged. It was a boy's paradise. We played at Victory Field, an abandoned grass airstrip used for pilot training during WWII, a big hangar with skeletal remains of old Piper Cubs. We made our own ball field in a vacant lot with a chicken-wire backstop and shot baskets in January, sliding around on frozen gravel driveways wearing cotton gloves with the fingertips cut off. Beyond the backyard gardens lay a twisting ravine, site of Civil War and Three Musketeers reenactments (*Sacre bleu, mon Dieu,* unhand that rapier!), that led to a stretch of sandy riverbank under the cottonwoods. Grown-ups seldom ventured there. We got to swim naked and skate on the river ice, but we were only five miles from the big city, which after the war was still a streetcar city—at the end of the line, the city stopped short; the cornfields began. From the 31st-floor observation deck of the Foshay Tower downtown, you saw farmland and silos to the north and west.

When I was 12, I rode my bike alone into the city, past the lumber mills, foundries, machine shops, barrel factory, and printing plants, along

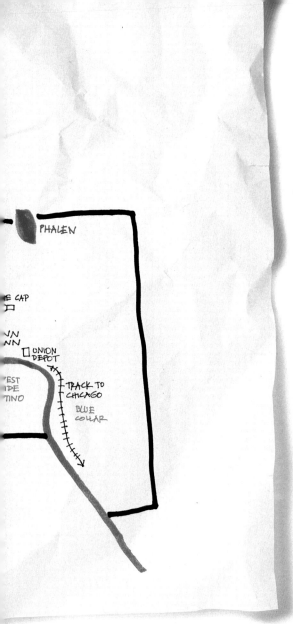

PHALEN

E CAP

VN
NN

ONION
DEPOT

EST
DE
TINO

TRACK TO
CHICAGO

BLUE
COLLAR

My crude map. The key to our geography is the river. Anyone can get lost trying to navigate the freeways through the suburbs, but once you find the Mississippi, you know where you are.

that changed my life—transformed, enriched, diversified, turned it topsy-turvy too—*Roget's International Thesaurus,* supplier of idiom, lingo, jargon, argot, blather, and phraseology that transformed me from nerd and nobody to visionary, sporting man, roughneck, bon vivant, and raconteur.

Growing up among the Brethren, a boy was ever aware of worldly temptation, and from that comes a keener perception of the world. A school field trip to the Milwaukee depot where the *Hiawatha* stood throbbing, waiting to depart for Chicago, steam hissing from the locomotive, the luxurious club car blue with cigar smoke from slick gents in three-piece suits—for the Brethren boy, an electric vision of worldly success and glamour. When I was 14, I got a tour of the art deco headquarters of the *Minneapolis Star* and *Tribune.* Upstairs, pencil-neck geeks tapping out copy and down below, the giant presses roaring, miles of newsprint flying out, chopped and folded into the evening *Star,* bundles of papers conveyed onto trucks and rushed to the readers, and the thought rang like a bell: I could be one of those guys upstairs. There were the neon lights of Hennepin Avenue and the promise of naked girls at the Alvin Theater, which our family passed on Sunday morning on our way to church, but that was lost on me, a geek with glasses, pressed pants, plaid shirt, a boy for whom dating girls was like exploring the Amazon—interesting idea, but how to get there? Writing for print, on the other hand—why not? And then came the beautiful connection: You write for print, it impresses girls, they might want to go on dates with you.

A boy named Frankie Renko drowned in the river one spring at the sandy bank where we boys hung out. I was eating supper when the fire truck went by, and I wanted to go see, but Mother said, "There's no point in a bunch

Washington Avenue and past a meatpacking plant where bare-chested men wrestled whole beef carcasses hung on hooks on little overhead trolleys along a rail and into the waiting trucks. I pedaled up Hennepin Avenue, past dirty-book stores, penny arcades, walk-up hotels, men slumped in doorways, to the magnificent old public library on Tenth across from White Castle, home of the ten-cent hamburger ("Buy 'em by the Sack"), and climbed up to the reading room, skipping the swimming lesson at the Y Mother had paid for so I'd learn to swim after cousin Roger drowned in Lake Minnetonka; but the Y conducted swim class in the nude and I was shy, so I went to the library instead and met the book

At the Brethren meeting hall in Anoka, a Sunday school class gathers under "A Chart on the Course of Time From Eternity to Eternity," the history of the cosmos summed up in a simple diagram.

Norma Koch is the perennial winner of the largest leaf contest at the annual Rhubarb Festival in Lanesboro. Rhubarb is the secret of the good life. But of course you knew that.

Sam Scott and Elyse Anton Roberts skating on the St. Croix River near Stillwater, both of them well brought up and therefore sensibly dressed. Winter is miserable only for people who don't know what to wear. True.

When I was young and mostly broke, I ate at White Castle, where less than a buck bought three little hamburgers and a cup of coffee and maybe a sad story from another patron, who needed bus fare to get to Wisconsin to see his ailing aunt. Lots of aunts in Wisconsin. And then he saw I was broke, and he turned away. But it was a good story.

of rubberneckers standing around gawking." She said it was unseemly to look upon the sufferings of others if you were powerless to help. Years later, a photographer at the *St. Paul Pioneer Press,* where I worked on the copydesk, writing obits, showed me his collection of pictures of dead people, drowned or shot or crushed in cars, but I did not look at them long. (I wanted to, but I didn't want him to think I was the sort of person who did.)

For days after Frankie drowned, I visited the death scene, trying to imagine what had happened. He was paddling a boat near the shore, and it capsized, and he drowned. I imagined this over and over, imagined myself saving him, imagined the vast gratitude of his family. I don't recall discussing this with other boys. We were more interested in what lay ahead in seventh grade, where (we had heard) you had to take showers after gym. Naked. With no clothes on. Which turned out to be true. Junior high was up the West River Road in Anoka, the town where I was born, 1942, in a house on Ferry Street, delivered by Dr. Mork. That fall of seventh grade, he listened to my heart and heard a click in the mitral valve, which meant I couldn't play football, so I walked into the *Anoka Herald* and asked for a job covering football and basketball, and a man named Warren Feist said yes and made me a professional writer. Ask and ye shall receive.

After seventh grade I was suddenly too old for the ravine and the riverbank. The next summer I worked on nearby truck farms, hoeing corn, picking potatoes. Other boys inherited the riverbank. I worked. At 18 I proceeded directly downriver to the University of Minnesota and the smoke-filled classrooms of Folwell Hall and football Saturdays and the blare of the glorious "Rouser" and old alums in their 40s lumbering lead-footed toward Memorial Stadium. I had literary ambitions—so did others—and we found each other and coalesced. We wrote dense jagged unreadable poems and exulted in obscurity, boys with long hair and girls with jiggly breasts under their aboriginal blouses, everyone skinny as snakes. I spent six years sorting through various personas (Boy Scholar, Embittered Poet,

Dangerous Radical, Wry Humorist) and wound up with the one that paid a salary: Friendly Announcer. I did all of this a couple miles from the Brethren, which made for interesting collisions. Standing outside the 400 Bar, smoking a Pall Mall, and a car honks, and it's Aunt Jean and Uncle Les. Drop the smoke, walk to the car, say hi, smile, try not to exhale. And now devout Muslims from Somalia live in the old Brethren neighborhood; robed women and somber elders watch teenage Somali girls go by in short shorts and daring tank tops and product in their hair. Same play, new actors.

From the U, I traipsed down the long winding trail of adulthood, walk-up apartments, dingy offices, cheap cafés, public library, softball diamonds, beer joints, and Grand Avenue, the street I drove down to work at 4 a.m. to do the morning shift on KSJN in a basement studio on Wabasha and then a storefront on Sixth Street, the house where I lived next to Luther Seminary and the backyard parties with musicians that inspired *A Prairie Home Companion* at Macalester College, the dramatic leap to home ownership on Cathedral Hill in St. Paul, where I've lived most of the last 20 years, where you drive up from I-94 past Masqueray's magnificent cathedral, whose great dome and towers and arches give you a momentary illusion of Europe, and up Summit and the mansions of 19th-century grandees and pooh-bahs in a ward that votes about 85 percent Democratic today.

You look out your kitchen window at a street from McKinley's America, and then three slender young women go running by, ponytails bouncing, wires coming out of their ears. In all, I count 26 places I've lived in the Twin Cities, about half on the west side of the river, half on the east, all within a few miles of downtown: A restless fugitive for 50 years, mostly within Hennepin and Ramsey Counties, now in a neighborhood where Mother, at 17, sold peanut butter cookies door-to-door during the Depression on a ridge above the river I loved as a boy. The *Empire Builder* rolls by a few blocks below me, my dad sorting mail, while my teenage mother comes to the door with bags of cookies, and my brother Phil and I paddle the wooden canoe we longed to own, and I am variously 12 and 43 and 71 years old: It's all conflated in my mind, like layers of a medieval town.

The Old Resident mourns for the Old City, though he understands that his classmates and cousins had babies and the metro area has more than twice as many people as in his 1950s childhood and everyone wanted to raise their kids in rambling houses with big leafy yards like the one he grew up in, not dinky apartments, and so the cornfields were given over to settlements of ramblers on curvy streets with romantic names like Yosemite Avenue, Emerald Trail, Everest Path, and Evening Star Way, and the earthmovers gouged out the interstates, the east-west 94, the north-south 35, and the downtowns dwindled and urban renewal wiped out whole blocks of Victorian stone edifices, old picture palaces,

then what they were thinking, and now I am old enough to know.

WHEN A MAN HAS LIVED in one place for most of his life, he walks around hip-deep in history. He sees that life is not so brief; it is vast and contains multitudes. I drive down Seventh Street to a Twins game and pass the old Dayton's department store (Macy's now but still Dayton's to me), where in my poverty days I shoplifted an unabridged dictionary the size of a suitcase, and 50 years later I still feel the terror of walking out the door with it under my jacket, and I imagine the cops arresting my 20-year-old self and what 30 days in the slammer might've done for me. From my seat above first base, I see the meatpacking plant where those men wrestled beef carcasses into trucks and the old Munsingwear factory with the low rumble and whine of

In 1947 Dad built us a little house on an acre of cornfield a stone's throw from the Mississippi.

department stores. And the planners created an infernal system of skyways—glass bridges connecting buildings at the second story—in effect turning buildings inside out, wiping out streets of little shops and show windows and the hopeful proprietors in favor of implacable corporations with brutal blank exteriors (he mourns this but learns not to see it). Instead, look up at the First National Bank building in St. Paul, the enormous "1st" on the roof outlined in flashing red neon—as a child, I thought it designated St. Paul as the number one city in America, a dazzling discovery for a boy who was brought up modest. Pride goeth before a fall, so deprecate yourself before others do the job for you. On the fourth-grade class trip to the capitol, we all stood on the roof of the bank, and I explained the significance of the "1" as a yellow streetcar rolled past a grassy square with a fountain in the middle, old men lounging on park benches, smoking, looking into the distance. I wondered

machines, and I remember an intense dread of spending one's days at a power loom making men's underwear. The building is today an enormous emporium of interior design showrooms, the place to go if you feel the urge to spend a hundred grand on a new bathroom, but to me it's still the coal mine I was afraid I'd spend my life in. I think about this along about the eighth inning if the Twins are down by a few runs.

When we graduated from Anoka High, my classmate Corinne Guntzel drove her dad's white Cadillac Eldorado convertible with rocket tail fins at high speed down the West River Road and into the city on a street just beyond right center field, and I stood in the front seat and sang, "That'll be the day, when you say goodbye / oh, that'll be the day, when you make me cry," and now she and her parents, Hilmar and Helen, lie in Crystal Lake Cemetery on the north side beyond left field, my stalwart friends and supporters, in the ground; thoughts of them click into

Saturday night in Hastings, and the owners of classic cars and trucks park them on the main drag for the curious to inspect. Leaning on this '58 Chevy pickup is Jessica Kuehl, who may or may not be a Hollywood film star.

A summer evening at Lake Calhoun, the
Minneapolis skyline to the east. When the
sun goes down and the swimmers go home,
and the sailors and canoeists, the lake takes
on a mystical aura, and you can imagine
it is 1834, and you are walking with Gideon
Pond, who is learning the language of the
Dakota, so he can preach the Gospel to them.

place whenever I pass the Dowling Avenue exit on 94. She was a suicide 28 years ago, drowned with rocks in her pockets, and I still love her and am not over her death, nor do I expect ever to be. If I drove by the cemetery with a visitor, I wouldn't say a word about this. Too much. Too painful. Her at the wheel, the summer wind in my face, the lights of Minneapolis passing, sweet love in the air. I would give the world to go back to that night and hold her in my arms.

I drive my little girl to school, a lovely ritual, and the route takes me through my Dangerous Radical years and past the place where my virginity went up in flames at age 22—the house replaced by an on-ramp to I-35W, the house that itself was an on-ramp to me—and past a steep slope below Ridgewood Avenue and the house where Mary and I decided not to be married anymore, only to find out that she was pregnant,

am telling the truth. And she laughs and laughs. My father never drove me to school. It was unheard of back then, so he never got to know me that well, just as he never wore his hair in a ponytail. Back in his day men who wore their hair in a ponytail were given electroshock therapy, which made them forget what day of the week it was. Today is Monday, and I am driving my daughter past Lake Calhoun, where, back in the ponytail era, I went skinny-dipping with a woman who now is a distinguished surgeon in town. If I ran into her today, I doubt that I'd mention it, and yet whenever I drive this way, memory gives me a glimpse of her excellent bare back and buttocks.

THE GREAT AMERICAN MYTH is the hero who leaves home to remake himself in another place: James Gatz leaves North Dakota to become Jay Gatsby of West Egg, Long Island; Robert Jordan

Mother said, "There is so much I'd still like to know, and there's nobody left to ask."

so we decided not to not be married. A bell tolls as I pass. My daughter says, "Tell me a story," so I tell her about riding the school bus in seventh grade, my gravel road the last stop, the bus packed with smelly children bundled in heavy mackinaws, no empty seats, nobody moving over, the whiskey-soaked bus driver yelling at me to sit down, dammit, which is maybe why I have such a poor self-image even today and flinch when people look at me and which naturally drove me into radio broadcasting instead of something more distinguished.

She says, "Tell me a funny story"—my daughter who never had to fight for a seat. I say, "So…there were these two penguins standing on an ice floe," and she says, "Tell the truth," so I say, "I like your ponytail. You know, years ago I wore my hair in a ponytail. Not a big ponytail. A little one. I had a beard too." And she looks at me. "A ponytail? Are you joking?" No, I did. It was only for a year or two, around 1972. And she realizes I

leaves his teaching job in Montana to fight in the Spanish Civil War; Huck Finn took a raft, Dorothy flew off in a tornado, Sister Carrie rode the train, Jack Kerouac hitched rides—and so forth—but in my experience the Cities have been quite roomy enough for a restless, impulsive person to live his life. I never felt stranded here. Sometimes I felt the pull of the roads going west, Highway 7 out of Excelsior and Clara City toward South Dakota, and Highway 212 through Chaska and Granite Falls, and Highway 12 through Litchfield and Willmar and Benson and Ortonville. And now and then, just for a taste of freedom, I'd drive out west late at night through the little towns and stop around 2 or 3 a.m. at a crossroad and get out of the car and walk around in the dark for a while and then head back to do my 6 a.m. radio shift.

After the university I spent part of a summer in New York City, thinking that a young writer ought to be there, but squalor did not appeal to me. I met an artist who painted by night and drove a cab by day, was hooked on marijuana and LSD, and lived in a tiny fourth floor walk-up with a wife and two little daughters. I decided that Minnesota was a better place to be poor. You can go to your mother's for a huge supper, and even if she doesn't approve of your life, she'll send you home with a big bag of vegetables from her garden. Also it was a better place to be original—behind the scrim of Midwesternness, the myth of the placid, backward hinterland—than in ferocious Manhattan.

WHEN MY MOTHER was nearing the end of her 97 years, what was most vivid to her was her youth. She said, "There is so much I'd still like to know, and there's nobody left to ask." So she ventured into the shadows to commune with her dead, which was a comfort to her. Nobody was alive who knew her in girlhood, so memory became reality. Some call it dementia, I call it imagination. At 71 I sometimes forget last week, but I clearly remember the big house on Dupont Avenue North where Corinne lived one summer when we were 19, and I blew smoke on her African violets to kill aphids. She and I had this idea to form a commune of writers all working away in their rooms, doors open, and when we wrote something good, we could walk into someone's room and tell them about it. A sort of long-term sleepover. It was a perfect idea, and we didn't bother with details such as Who and Where and How much, and because it never became a reality, it never came crashing down. It still exists in my mind. If I reach 97, I may finally go live there.

My mother died in the front bedroom of the house Dad built in the cornfield after the war. He died in that room too, 11 years before her. It had been my bedroom. I used to sit on the bed and smoke, gazing at the red blinking light on a distant water tower, and imagine living in New York. My parents were very clear that they wished to die in their old house and not in a hospital. They wanted family to be with them at the end, holding their hands and singing, "Abide with me; fast falls the eventide," and

"Then we shall be where we would be, Then we shall be what we should be," as they passed to their heavenly home. The bedroom looks out on the driveway where Dad's Ford station wagon used to be parked, ready to leave early the next morning to drive to Idaho to visit relatives. My mother stayed up late, washing, ironing, packing and repacking, in an ecstasy of anxiety. My father changed the oil, checked tire pressures, adjusted the timing. At sunrise, we were washed and combed, ready to go, and stood on the front lawn, watching him pack the car. They made a good team. He was laconic and undaunted, she was prone to excitation. We headed west on Highway 12, the rising sun to our backs, as she deliberated the perpetual question: Had she turned the oven off? And decided she had—and out onto the open prairie we went, with me sitting behind Mother narrating the trip from the old Federal Writers' state guide. Now they're buried in a little country cemetery full of aunts and uncles, grandparents, great-grandparents, and someday, I presume, cousins and siblings.

"So how was it to grow up there then?" they say. "Oh, you know. It could've been worse," I reply. We are not braggarts and blowhards back where I come from. But if you want to know the truth, I feel understood there. I sit down to lunch with Bill and Bob or my sister and brother whom I've known almost forever, and it's a conversation you can't have with people you met yesterday. You can flash back to 1954 and the island in the river where we used to mess around, or the front office you shared with Warren Feist that looked across the street to the Anoka Dairy, or the toboggan slope behind Corinne's house, no footnote necessary, and they are right there with you. I come home and feel so well understood. I almost don't have to say a word. I was not a good person. I have yelled at my children. I neglected my parents and was disloyal to loved ones. I have offended righteous people. People around here know all this about me, and yet they still smile and say hello, and so every day I feel forgiven. Ask me if it's a good place to live, and I don't know—that's real estate talk—but forgiveness and understanding, that's a beautiful combination. ☐

The dome of the Cathedral of Santa Maria del Fiore in Florence, Italy, was completed in 1436. Its supple curves and innovative engineering are a monument to the genius of Filippo Brunelleschi.

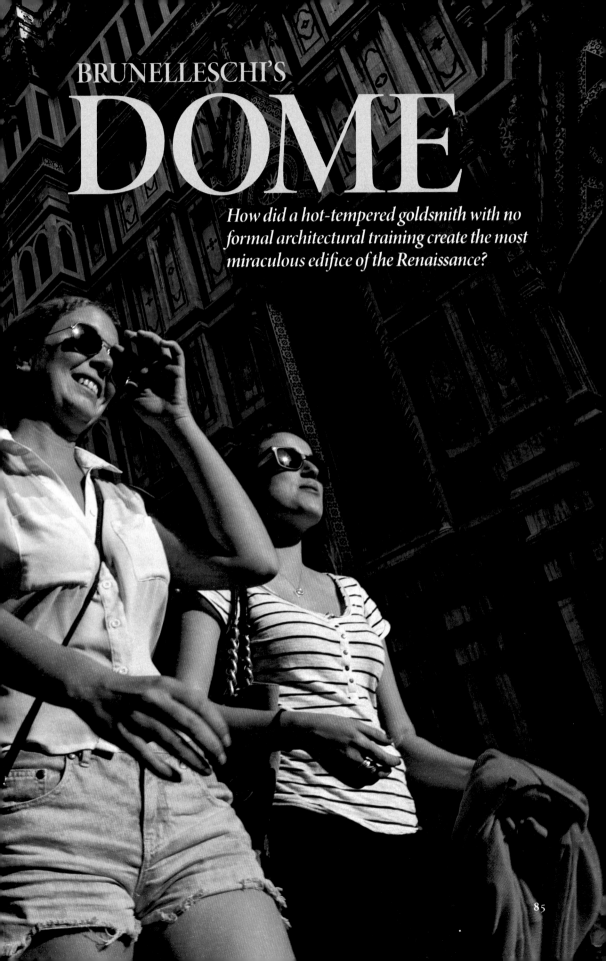

BRUNELLESCHI'S
DOME

How did a hot-tempered goldsmith with no formal architectural training create the most miraculous edifice of the Renaissance?

Begun in the medieval era, in 1296, the Florence cathedral is mostly Gothic, with pointed arches and angular vertical spaces. By the time Brunelleschi began work on the dome 124 years later, the style was passé.

By Tom Mueller

Photographs by Dave Yoder

I n 1418 the town fathers of Florence finally addressed a monumental problem they'd been ignoring for decades: the enormous hole in the roof of their cathedral. Season after season, the winter rains and summer sun had streamed in over Santa Maria del Fiore's high altar—

or where the high altar should have been. Their predecessors had begun the church in 1296 to showcase the status of Florence as one of Europe's economic and cultural capitals, grown rich on high finance and the wool and silk trades. It was later decided that the structure's crowning glory would be the largest cupola on Earth, ensuring the church would be "more useful and beautiful, more powerful and honorable" than any other ever built, as the grandees of Florence decreed.

Still, many decades later, no one seemed to have a viable idea of how to build a dome nearly 150 feet across, especially as it would have to start 180 feet above the ground, atop the existing walls. Other questions plagued the cathedral overseers. Their building plans eschewed the flying buttresses and pointed arches of the traditional Gothic style then favored by rival northern cities like Milan, Florence's archenemy.

Yet these were the only architectural solutions known to work in such a vast structure. Could a dome weighing tens of thousands of tons stay up without them? Was there enough timber in Tuscany for the scaffolding and templates that would be needed to shape the dome's masonry? And could a dome be built at all on the octagonal floor plan dictated by the existing walls— eight pie-shaped wedges—without collapsing inward as the masonry arced toward the apex? No one knew.

So in 1418 the worried Florentine fathers announced a contest for the ideal dome design, with a handsome prize of 200 gold florins—and a shot at eternal fame—for the winner. Leading architects of the age flocked to Florence and presented their ideas. From start to finish, the project was so charged with doubts, fears, creative secrecy, and civic pride that a lush tapestry of legend was woven around it, turning the story of the cupola into a parable of Florentine ingenuity and a central creation myth of the Italian Renaissance.

When the first histories were written, the losers came off particularly poorly. One contending

Tom Mueller is author of the recently published Extra Virginity: The Sublime and Scandalous World of Olive Oil. *Dave Yoder is a photographer and National Geographic explorer based in Milan.*

Brunelleschi designed his masterpiece as two domes, one inside the other. While not admired for their artistry, the Last Judgment scenes painted on the inner dome by Vasari and Zuccaro are among the largest paintings on Earth.

Milan • Venice •
ITALY
Pisa • **Florence**
Rome ★
Naples •
Tuscany
Adriatic Sea
Tyrrhenian Sea
Mediterranean Sea

0 mi   100
0 km 100

architect, it was said, proposed to support the dome with an enormous pillar rising in the center of the church. Another suggested building it out of "sponge-stone" (perhaps *spugna,* a porous volcanic rock) to minimize its weight. Yet another, according to early legend, proposed that a mountain of dirt mixed with coins serve as scaffolding, to be cleared away free of charge by the money-grubbing citizenry after the dome was complete.

What we know for sure is that another candidate, a short, homely, and hot-tempered

> *Brunelleschi was forced to work with his gallingly successful rival. The arrangement would lead to much plotting and skulduggery.*

goldsmith named Filippo Brunelleschi, promised to build not one but two domes, one nested inside the other, without elaborate and expensive scaffolding. Yet he refused to explain how he'd achieve this, fearing that a competitor would steal his ideas. Brunelleschi's stubbornness led to a shouting match with the overseers, who twice had him restrained and forcibly ejected from the assembly, denouncing him as "a buffoon and a babbler."

Nonetheless, Brunelleschi's mysterious design piqued their imagination—perhaps because they already knew this buffoon and babbler to be a genius. As a boy, during his goldsmith's apprenticeship, he had mastered drawing and painting, wood carving, sculpture in silver and bronze, stone setting, niello, and enamel work. Later he studied optics and tinkered endlessly with wheels, gears, weights, and motion, building a number of ingenious clocks, including what may have been one of the first alarm clocks in history. Applying his theoretical and mechanical knowledge to observation of the natural world, he single-handedly worked out the rules of linear perspective. He'd just spent several years in Rome

measuring and sketching the ancient monuments and noting, in cipher, their architectural secrets. Indeed, Brunelleschi's life seemed to have been one long apprenticeship for building the dome of unequaled beauty, usefulness, honor, and power that Florence yearned for.

The next year the overseers met with Brunelleschi several times, eliciting more details of his scheme. They began to realize just how brilliant (and risky) it really was. His dome would consist of two concentric shells, an inner one visible from within the cathedral nested inside a wider, taller external dome. To counteract "hoop stress," the outward, bulging pressure created by a large structure's weight that could cause it to crack or collapse, he would bind the walls with tension rings of stone, iron, and wood, like hoops on a barrel. He'd build the first 46 feet in stone, he said, after which he would continue with lighter materials, either spugna or brick. He also assured the overseers that he could do without conventional, ground-based scaffolding. They welcomed the enormous savings in lumber and labor that would result, at least during work on the first 57 feet, after which everything would depend on how things went, "because in building, only practical experience will teach that which is to be followed."

IN 1420 THE OVERSEERS agreed to make Filippo Brunelleschi the *provveditore,* or superintendent, of the cupola project. They added one significant caveat. Being hardheaded merchants and bankers who believed in competition as a way of ensuring quality control, they appointed Lorenzo Ghiberti, Brunelleschi's fellow goldsmith, as a co-superintendent. The two men had been rivals since 1401, when they had vied for another illustrious commission, the new bronze doors for the Florentine Baptistery. Ghiberti had won. (Much later, an admiring Michelangelo would refer to a second set of Ghiberti's doors as "the Gates of Paradise.") By this time, Ghiberti was the most illustrious and politically connected artist in Florence. Now Brunelleschi, whose design for the cupola had been accepted outright, was forced to work side by side with his gallingly successful rival. The arrangement would lead to much plotting and skulduggery.

On this tempestuous note began the building of Il Cupolone (the Big Dome), a monumental project whose growth over the next 16 years became the city's drama in miniature. The dome's progress was a reference point for life in the city—events were predicted to occur and promises were to be kept "before the Dome is covered." Its looming, rounded profile, so unlike the angular lines of the Gothic, symbolized the Florentine Republic's freedom from tyrannous Milan, and even more so, the nascent Renaissance's liberation from the airless constraints of the Middle Ages.

THE FIRST PROBLEM to be solved was purely technical: No known lifting mechanisms were capable of raising and maneuvering the enormously heavy materials he had to work with, including sandstone beams, so far off the ground. Here Brunelleschi the clockmaker and tinkerer outdid himself. He invented a three-speed hoist with an intricate system of gears, pulleys, screws, and driveshafts, powered by a single yoke of oxen turning a wooden tiller. It used a special rope 600 feet long and weighing over a thousand pounds—custom-made by shipwrights in Pisa—and featured a groundbreaking clutch system that could reverse direction without having to turn the oxen around. Later Brunelleschi made other innovative lifting machines, including the *castello*, a 65-foot-tall crane with a series of counterweights and hand screws to move loads laterally once they'd been raised to the right height. Brunelleschi's lifts were so far ahead of their time that they weren't rivaled until the industrial revolution, though they did fascinate generations of artists and inventors, including a certain Leonardo from the nearby Tuscan town of Vinci, whose sketchbooks tell us how they were made.

Having assembled the necessary tool kit, Brunelleschi turned his full attention to the dome itself, which he shaped with a series of stunning technical innovations. His double-shell design yielded a structure that was far lighter and loftier than a solid dome of such size would have been. He wove regular courses of herringbone brickwork, little known before his time, into the texture of the cupola, giving the entire structure additional solidity.

Throughout the years of construction Brunelleschi spent more and more time on the work site. He oversaw the production of bricks of various dimensions and attended to the supply of choice stone and marble from the quarries. He led an army of masons and stonecutters, carpenters, blacksmiths, lead beaters, barrelmakers, water carriers, and other craftsmen. When they were puzzled by some tricky construction detail, one biographer tells us, he'd shape a model out of wax or clay or carve up a turnip to illustrate what he wanted. Brunelleschi took particular care of his workers, both for their safety and to ensure that the dome progressed as rapidly as possible. He ordered that their wine be cut with water to keep them sharp on the heights (this provision was revoked under pressure by dissatisfied workers) and added parapets to the suspended platforms to prevent them from falling—or looking down from the dizzying height of the dome. According to popular legend, Brunelleschi could also be a hard taskmaster. When masons went on strike demanding better pay, we are told, he called in scabs from Lombardy, and relented only when the masons returned, hats in hand, and agreed to resume their jobs—at reduced wages.

He also had to contend with highly placed adversaries, led by the scheming Lorenzo Ghiberti. Brunelleschi was the project's conceptual and operational leader from the start, yet he and Ghiberti received the same yearly wage of 36 florins. Brunelleschi's biographers tell an amusing tale about how he finally outmaneuvered Ghiberti. In the summer of 1423, just before a wooden tension ring was to be laid around the dome, Brunelleschi suddenly took to his bed, complaining of severe pains in his side. When the baffled carpenters and masons asked how they were to position the enormous chestnut beams that made up the ring, he essentially delegated

OROMO

DUOMO

BOTEGA DEGLI ANIMALI

Like a presiding spirit, the cathedral—duomo in Italian— keeps watch over the streetscapes of Florence, including this block of Via dei Servi, a few hundred yards northeast of the church.

The original gilded copper orb on the dome was designed, cast, and set in place between 1466 and 1471. Lightning destroyed it around 1600. Today's orb is protected by a modern system of lightning rods.

the task to his rival. Ghiberti had installed only some of the beams when Brunelleschi, miraculously on the mend, returned to the work site and pronounced Ghiberti's work so incompetent that it would have to be torn out and replaced. Brunelleschi directed these repairs himself, complaining all the while to the overseers that his co-superintendent was earning a salary he didn't deserve. Though this account may be tinged by hero worship, archival records at year's end do name Brunelleschi the sole "inventor and director of the cupola," and later his salary rose to a hundred florins a year, while Ghiberti continued at 36 florins.

Ghiberti didn't give in. Around 1426 his assistant, the architect Giovanni da Prato, sent the overseers a large piece of vellum, still preserved in the National Archives of Florence, on which he'd penned a detailed criticism of Brunelleschi's work, complete with illustrations. He claimed that Brunelleschi, through "ignorance and presumption," had deviated from the original plans for the cupola, which was therefore "spoiled and put in danger of ruin."

Giovanni also composed a violent personal attack on Brunelleschi in sonnet form. The poem calls Brunelleschi a "dark, deep wellspring of ignorance" and a "miserable and imbecile beast" whose plans were doomed to failure. If they ever succeeded, Giovanni rather rashly promised, he would kill himself. Brunelleschi replied with a barbed sonnet of his own, warning Giovanni to destroy his poems, "lest they sound ridiculous when all the dancing starts, in celebration of that which he now thinks impossible."

Brunelleschi and his workmen eventually did their victory dance, though only after several more years of doubt and struggle. In 1429 cracks appeared in the east end of the cathedral nave beside the dome, forcing Brunelleschi to shore up the walls with iron tie bars. In 1434, perhaps at Ghiberti's instigation, Brunelleschi was jailed on a technicality regarding unpaid union dues. But soon after, he was released, and the cupola continued skyward at the average rate of about one foot per month. On March 25, 1436, the Feast of the Annunciation, Pope Eugenius IV and an assembly of cardinals and bishops consecrated the finished cathedral, to the tolling of bells and cheering of proud Florentines. A decade later another illustrious group laid the cornerstone of the lantern, the decorative marble structure that Brunelleschi designed to crown his masterpiece.

Soon after, on April 15, 1446, Brunelleschi died, apparently from a sudden illness. At his funeral he lay dressed in white linen on a bier ringed by candles, staring sightlessly into the dome he had built brick by brick, as the candle smoke and the notes of the funeral dirge spiraled into the void. He was buried in the crypt of the cathedral; a memorial plaque nearby celebrated his "divine intellect." These were high honors. Before Brunelleschi's time, very few people, among them a saint, were allowed burial in the crypt, and architects were mostly considered humble craftsmen. With genius, leadership, and grit, Filippo Brunelleschi raised true artists to the rank of sublime creators, worthy of eternal praise in the company of the saints, an image that would dominate the Renaissance.

In fact, he paved the way for the cultural and social revolutions of the Renaissance itself, through his complex synthesis of inspiration and analysis, his bold reworking of the classical past to the needs and aspirations of the present. Once complete, Santa Maria del Fiore was decorated by artists like Donatello, Paolo Uccello, and Luca Della Robbia, making it both the birthplace and the proving ground of the Renaissance. Brunelleschi's dome still rises from the terra-cotta sea of Florence's roof tiles, itself terra-cotta clad yet harmoniously proportioned, like a Greek goddess in homespun. It is mountainous yet strangely buoyant, as if the white marble ridges rising to its apex are ropes holding a zeppelin to Earth. Somehow Brunelleschi captured freedom in stone, exalting the Florentine skyline ever after with an upward-yearning embodiment of the human spirit. ☐

HOW DID HE DO IT?

A grand engineering experiment led by scholar Massimo Ricci reveals how Brunelleschi built his dome, on *Great Cathedral Mystery*, February 12 on NOVA/PBS.

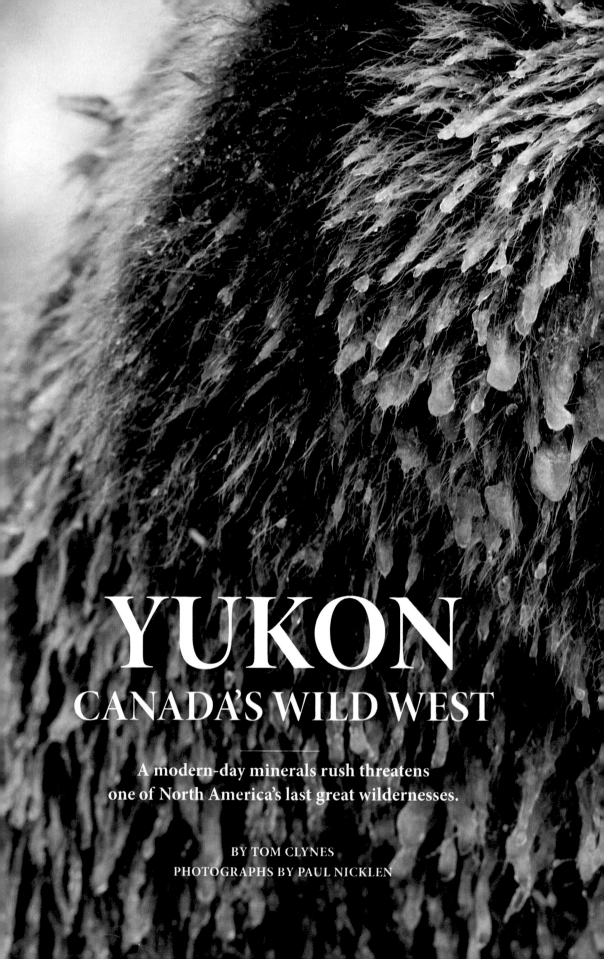

YUKON
CANADA'S WILD WEST

A modern-day minerals rush threatens
one of North America's last great wildernesses.

BY TOM CLYNES
PHOTOGRAPHS BY PAUL NICKLEN

Having gorged on salmon to lay on fat for hibernation, a grizzly wears a coat of ice.

The Yukon's backcountry hides sublime surprises, such as Azure Lake in the rugged Ogilvie Mountains. Glacial meltwater laden with fine sediment lends the lake its namesake color.

Along the Porcupine River caribou have been a mainstay of the Vuntut Gwitchin people for at least 10,000 years. Now development is threatening their traditional way of life.

Gold fever first struck the Yukon in the 1890s.

Shawn Ryan recalls the hungry years, before his first big strike.

The prospector and his family were living in a metal shack on the outskirts of Dawson, the Klondike boomtown that had declined to a ghostly remnant of its glory days. They had less than $300 and no running water or electricity. One night, as wind sneaked through gaps in the cladding, Ryan's wife, Cathy Wood, worried aloud that their two children might even freeze to death.

Today the couple could buy—and heat—just about any house on Earth. Ryan's discovery of what would eventually amount to billions of dollars' worth of buried treasure has helped reinfect the Yukon with gold fever, and fortune seekers have stormed the Canadian territory in numbers not seen since the 1890s.

The minerals rush has reanimated Dawson's weather-tilted bars and bunkhouses, whose facades glow in pastel hues during midsummer's late-night sunset. The scene could be from more than a century ago, with bearded men bustling along wooden sidewalks and muddy streets, hooting and trading rumors of the latest strikes and price spikes. Inside Diamond Tooth Gerties casino, miners mingle with tourists and cancan girls, thronging four deep around beer taps and poker tables.

During the first Klondike stampede prospectors plied nearby creeks with picks and pans and shovels, and a bartender could sweep up a small fortune in spilled gold dust at the end of a big night. Nowadays mining's heavy lifting is done by a mechanized army of bulldozers, drilling rigs, and flown-in workers. The claim-staking boom has cooled since the price of gold has stabilized, but an ongoing high demand for minerals and the Yukon's industry-friendly regulations continue to attract mining companies from as far away as China.

At Shawn Ryan's expanding compound at the edge of town, helicopters thump overhead, fetching GPS-equipped prospectors to and from remote mountain ridges. Ryan is 50 years old, but he radiates the eagerness and intensity of a much younger man. "This is the biggest geochemical exploration project on the planet right now," he says, his grin revealing a couple of missing upper teeth, "and maybe in history."

In the modular office he calls his war room, radios and bear-spray canisters surround a trio of computer screens atop a plywood table. A self-taught geologist, Ryan uses the left-hand screen to display the colored maps he generates from his ever growing database of soil samples, looking for anomalies that might betray a hidden body of precious ore. On the center screen a blue grid overlays a map of the Yukon, showing the claims he currently owns; since 1996 he and

A bird's-eye view takes in only a fraction of the vast Faro Mine Complex, once the world's largest open-pit lead-zinc mine and now the target of a costly taxpayer-funded cleanup.

his crews have staked more than 55,000 claims, enough to cover a landmass larger than Jamaica. Ryan uses the right-side screen to track his gold-related holdings, which notch up in value whenever an economic jolt sends investors fleeing to precious metals.

As the material needs of the world's seven billion people continue to grow, the rush to exploit the Yukon's exceptionally rich resources—gold, zinc, copper, and more—has brought prosperity to a once forsaken corner of the continent. But the boom has brought to the fore a growing tension between those who would keep one of North America's last great wildernesses unbroken and those whose success depends on digging it up.

"They're blanket-staking the whole territory," says Trish Hume, a member of the Champagne and Aishihik First Nations. Though Hume does mapping work that's mining related, she worries that the Yukon is reaching a tipping point where the environmental and cultural costs of mining outweigh the benefits. "The people coming up and taking out minerals aren't asking what happens to the animals we hunt, the fish we eat, the topsoil that holds it all together. And when the boom is over, how does our tiny population afford to clean up the toxic mess?"

LARGER THAN CALIFORNIA but with only 37,000 inhabitants, the Yukon drives an immense wedge between Alaska and the bulk of Canada. From its north coast on the Beaufort Sea, it stretches to the south and southeast, taking in tremendous expanses of lake-dotted tundra, forests, mountains, wetlands, and river systems. Walled off by some of Canada's highest peaks and largest glaciers, the territory is almost completely unsettled, its sparse population scattered over a few small communities and the capital, Whitehorse. It is also rich in wildlife, an Arctic Serengeti whose extreme seasonal shifts beckon vast herds of caribou and other animals into motion. Among its wildest quarters is the Peel watershed, an immense wilderness, which drains an area larger than Scotland.

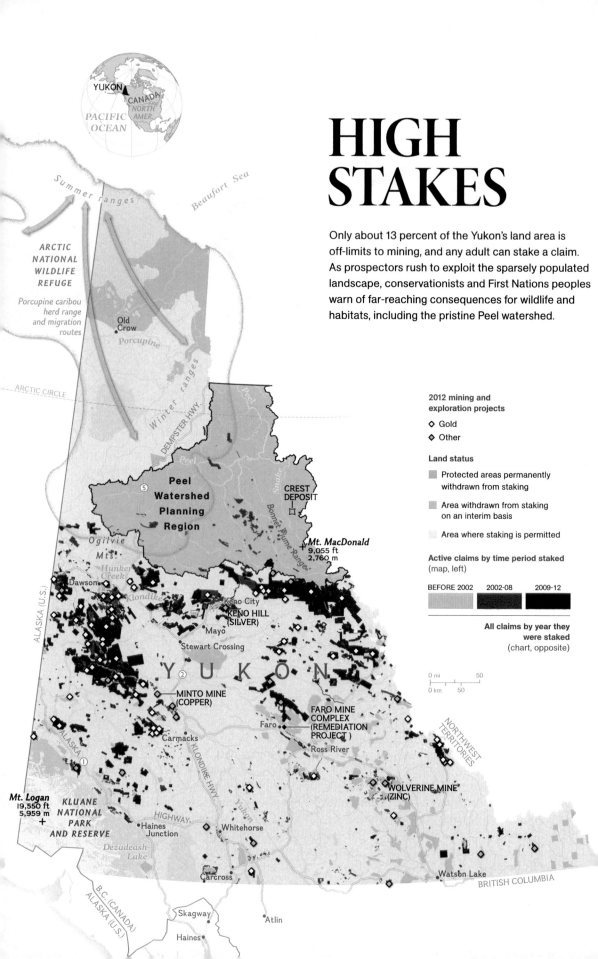

HIGH STAKES

Only about 13 percent of the Yukon's land area is off-limits to mining, and any adult can stake a claim. As prospectors rush to exploit the sparsely populated landscape, conservationists and First Nations peoples warn of far-reaching consequences for wildlife and habitats, including the pristine Peel watershed.

STAKING SOARS WITH GOLD PRICES

The year 2011 saw more than 115,000 mining claims, the peak of an intense rush. The driving factors were high prices for commodities—chiefly gold—aided by industry-friendly regulations and tax policies, and streamlined environmental risk assessments. Staking fever has since cooled as companies secure claims and confirm deposits.

BATTLE OVER WILDERNESS ZONING

Sprawling over 26,000 square miles, the Peel watershed is one of the largest wild areas remaining in North America. A 2011 zoning plan (below right) would have maintained the area's wilderness character, but since then the Yukon government has proposed a plan more favorable to industrial development.

2011: 115,158 claims—

Ecological assets of the Peel Watershed Planning Region

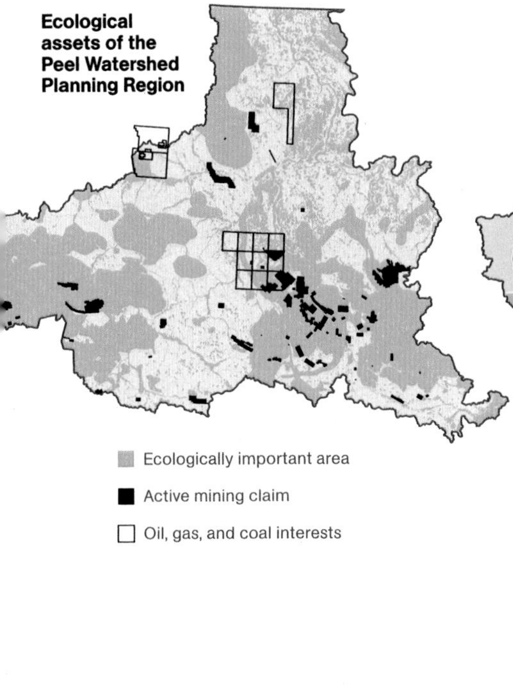

Planning commission's 2011 zoning proposal

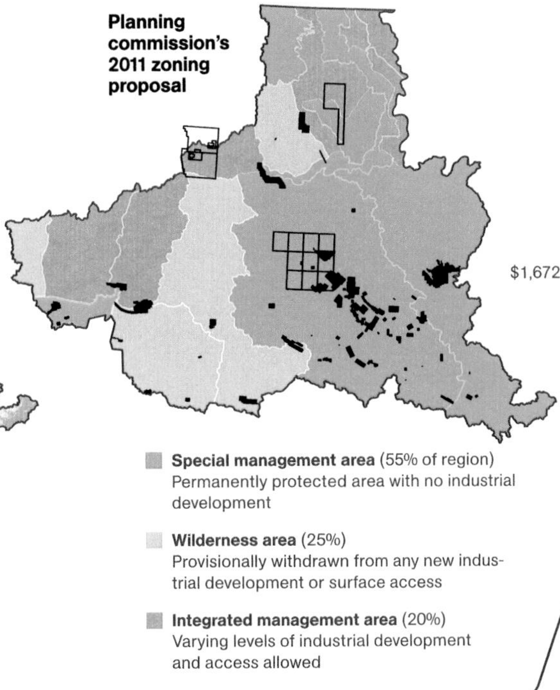

$1,672/oz—

■ Ecologically important area

■ Active mining claim

☐ Oil, gas, and coal interests

■ **Special management area** (55% of region)
Permanently protected area with no industrial development

■ **Wilderness area** (25%)
Provisionally withdrawn from any new industrial development or surface access

■ **Integrated management area** (20%)
Varying levels of industrial development and access allowed

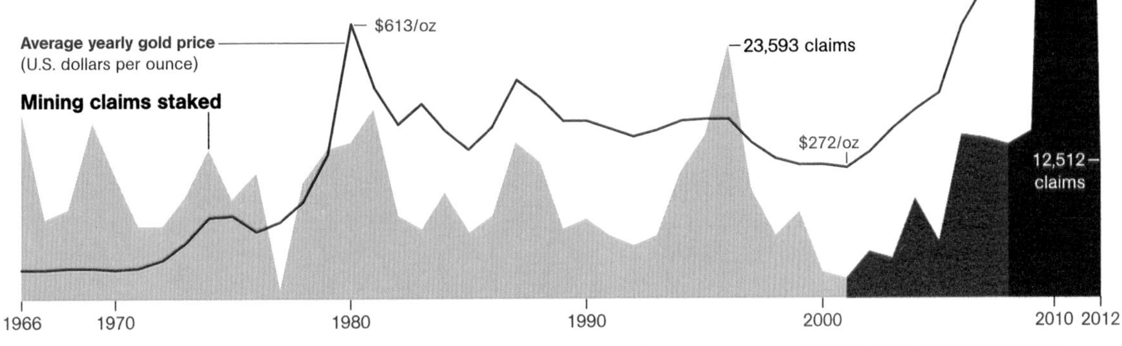

— $613/oz

Average yearly gold price—
(U.S. dollars per ounce)

Mining claims staked

—23,593 claims

$272/oz

12,512—claims

1966   1970   1980   1990   2000   2010 2012

MARTIN GAMACHE, NGM STAFF. SOURCES: ENERGY, MINES AND RESOURCES, YUKON; ENVIRONMENT YUKON; GEOMATICS YUKON; PEEL WATERSHED PLANNING COMMISSION; USGS; YUKON CONSERVATION SOCIETY; YUKON LAND USE PLANNING COUNCIL

Wild heart of the Yukon Territory, the Peel watershed is rich in rugged peaks and braided rivers. It also harbors vast mineral wealth, sparking fierce debate over its future.

Surface mining has transformed Hunker Creek into a wasteland. Massive machines do the work, but many mining laws date from the pick-and-shovel days.

"The Peel watershed is one of the few places left where you still have large, intact predator-prey ecosystems," says Karen Baltgailis of the Yukon Conservation Society. "From wolves and grizzlies and eagles on down, it's a wildlife habitat of global importance."

The Yukon has long served as a migration waypoint for humans too. During the last glacial period, when most of Canada was buried under a mile of ice, Alaska and the Yukon were part of an arid, glacier-free pocket called Beringia, which linked Siberia and North America. Animal bones discovered in the Yukon's Arctic and carbon dated to 25,000 years and older appear, to some archaeologists, to have been broken or cut by humans—though many scholars contest this claim. It's clear, however, that human populations were permanently established by about 13,000 years ago, when retreating glaciers opened up corridors that allowed people to migrate north and south.

These nomadic hunters brought elements of their culture and technology with them. Eventually Dene (sometimes referred to as Athabaskan)

languages became widespread. Even now, Navajo and Apache speakers in the American Southwest share words and sentence structures with many of the Yukon's First Nations peoples, despite centuries of separation.

The Yukon's early inhabitants hunted bison, elk, caribou, woolly mammoths, waterfowl, and fish, and they competed for resources with carnivores such as wolves and Beringian lions. Due to climate warming and other factors, some of these animals died off. But others, such as the barren-ground caribou, thrived in such numbers that native peoples adapted their own movements and lifestyles to the animals' migrations.

"We've been depending on the caribou for at least 10,000 years," says Norma Kassi, former chief of the Vuntut Gwitchin First Nation. "Our oral tradition tells us that a Gwitchin man sealed a pact of coexistence by trading a piece of his own beating heart for one from a living caribou."

The Porcupine caribou herd is named after the big westward-flowing river that many of the animals cross twice each year. Their journey begins 400 miles to the northwest in Alaska's Arctic National Wildlife Refuge (ANWR). Each spring more than 100,000 caribou converge on the coastal plain to gorge on protein-rich cotton grass. Massing in groups of tens of thousands, the cows give birth almost in unison—possibly a "swamping" strategy that allows the majority of calves to survive the predations of grizzly bears, wolves, and golden eagles.

When the calves are just a few weeks old, the herd begins to move south, a cacophony of clacking hooves, bellowing cows, and bleating calves. Though the adults' towering antlers give them a top-heavy, somewhat comical appearance, caribou are among nature's most graceful travelers, custom-built for their journey across mountain ranges and rivers into the windswept marshland that is the traditional hunting ground of the Vuntut Gwitchin.

THE SNOW IS FLYING as my plane banks over the Porcupine River and touches down in Old Crow, the Yukon's northernmost community. Unconnected by roads to the rest of the world, the village is a jumble of raised wooden houses whose outer walls are decorated with caribou and moose antlers.

The Gwitchin are among the last people in North America who meet most of their nutritional needs by hunting and gathering. Through the slats of smokehouses, I can see strings of drying meat and fish. The caribou are due to begin moving through the area at any moment, and the mood of the village is energized and upbeat. Barrel-chested men pilot all-terrain vehicles through snowy gusts, and children run around in T-shirts chasing sled-dog puppies.

Robert Bruce, a genial, Santa-like man in his 60s, rides up on an ATV, a smile stretching across his broad face. "The caribou!" he yells. "They're here!"

A few minutes later we're inside his house eating caribou stew, talking of the herd's long-awaited arrival, and sharing family history. Bruce grew up on the land, moving with the seasons to harvest wild game, fish, and berries. Though he, like most Gwitchin men, still hunts

or fishes nearly every day, life in Old Crow is not primitive. A village store offers expensive packaged food flown in from Whitehorse, and satellite television and the Internet have enabled the Gwitchin to see themselves in the context of the wider world. Alcohol is banned, but substance abuse and identity issues have had profound effects on the community, especially young people.

Using bicycles, a beat-up boat, and mostly their own feet, the two men began to home in on millions of ounces of gold.

As we talk, Bruce's adolescent grandson, Tyrel, sprawls on the couch, half watching a *Three's Company* rerun. "Tomorrow," Bruce says, winking, "we'll take him hunting."

The government had claimed nearly all of the Yukon territory as crown land. A hard-fought land-claims process recently returned control of some of the land to its native inhabitants, allowing them to again be the guardians of the places where they travel, hunt, and fish. But some threats, such as climate change, are outside the community's sphere of influence. "See those riverbanks collapsing?" Bruce says as he steers his aluminum motorboat upstream. "That's the permafrost thawing. Ten years ago we'd have ice on the river by this time. And now we have animals like cougars coming here, and new plants that cover our blueberries and rose hips. That's where we always got our vitamins."

Like other Gwitchin elders, Bruce has traveled to Washington and elsewhere in the U.S., appealing to the American people to protect the Porcupine herd's calving grounds. Politicians have tried multiple times to open ANWR's coastal plain to oil and gas leasing. Drilling could tap a reservoir of billions of barrels of oil—and, biologists say, displace the caribou from their core calving grounds. "We call it *vadzaih googii vi dehk'it gwanlii*," Bruce tells me, "the sacred place

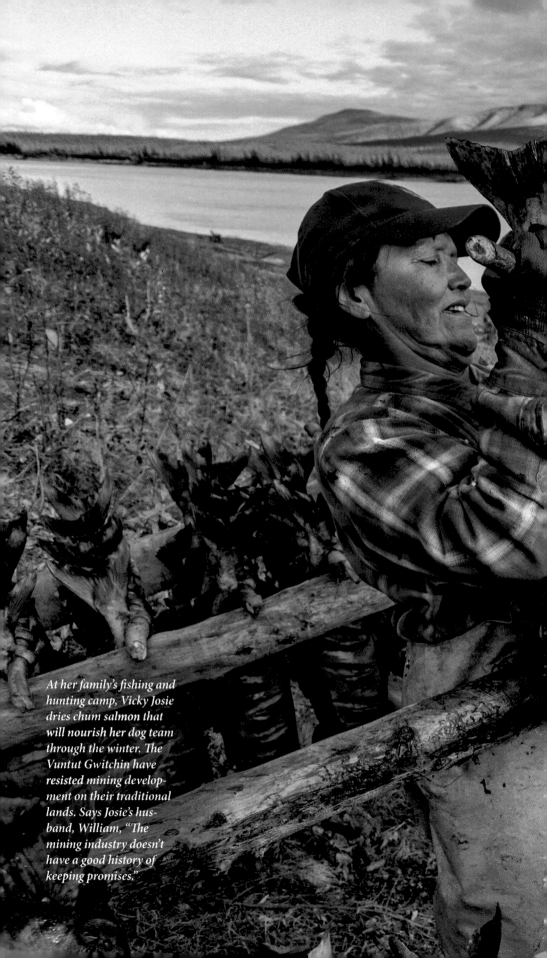

At her family's fishing and hunting camp, Vicky Josie dries chum salmon that will nourish her dog team through the winter. The Vuntut Gwitchin have resisted mining development on their traditional lands. Says Josie's husband, William, "The mining industry doesn't have a good history of keeping promises."

Caribou begin their
epic journey from
calving grounds in
Alaska's Arctic
National Wildlife
Refuge to their Yukon
wintering grounds.

Wolf pups come out of their den and sniff the spring air. Despite a history of bounties, culling from airplanes, and other measures, an estimated 5,000 wolves roam the territory.

where life begins. To us, it's a human rights issue. Because when the caribou are gone, our culture is gone."

In a few minutes Bruce squints and guns the motor. "Caribou!" he yells, reaching for his rifle. Moments later he pulls up alongside a swimming herd of six, selects a bull in mid-pack—"We never take the leaders," he says—and dispatches it with a shot to the neck. It's not the sort of hunting that would pass the test of sportsmanship farther south. To a Gwitchin, though, hunting isn't recreation; it's a means of acquiring protein and fat in a place where efficiency has always meant survival.

As Tyrel grabs hold of the caribou's antlers and Bruce steers the boat toward shore, I realize that something's not right. It's autumn, but this herd was headed north. "We're seeing more of that now," Bruce says, as he swipes his knife

Tom Clynes is author of the forthcoming book The Boy Who Played With Fusion. *Photographer Paul Nicklen lived in the Yukon for much of his adult life.*

blade across a sharpening stone. "Caribou are smart, smart as humans. But we've gotten confused, and now the caribou are getting confused too. So many changes."

WITH THEIR light-on-the-feet lifestyle, native Yukoners saw little value in the heavy metal they noticed sparkling at the bottom of sunlit creeks. Prospectors began poking around the Yukon in the 1870s, but it wasn't until 1896 that three miners dipped their pans into a creek near the confluence of the Yukon and Klondike Rivers. News of the strike finally reached civilization 11 months later, when the first newly rich miners descended gangplanks in San Francisco and Seattle, staggering under the weight of their riches. Within days headlines around the world were screaming, "Gold! Gold! Gold!…Stacks of Yellow Metal!"

Thus began one of the most extraordinary outbreaks of mass hysteria in modern history. The term "stampede" was a fitting and quite literal description, as tens of thousands stormed the ticket offices of the steamboat companies that were heavily promoting the Klondike's get-rich-quick possibilities and struck out toward a wilderness for which few were prepared.

"My father said they came like mosquitoes," says Percy Henry, 86, an elder in the Tr'ondëk Hwëch'in First Nation. "Isaac, our chief, said that they would destroy our land—and that there was nothing we could do to stop them."

The newcomers converged on a soggy flood-plain that the Tr'ondëk Hwech'in had used as a fishing and hunting camp. Within months the nearby forests had been cut down, and tens of thousands of stampeders were digging in nearby creeks. By the summer of 1898 Dawson City was a rough-hewn metropolis of 30,000, with telephones, running water, and electric lights.

And then, even more quickly than it had begun, it was over. In 1899, a year after Dawson was declared the capital of the newly founded Yukon Territory, word of a new strike in Nome, Alaska, drew many miners downstream on the Yukon River. Others, bent by scurvy and drained by the realization that their dreams had come to nothing, sold what they could and headed home. Over the next decades a few men found work on the gold dredges that began to work the rivers and dammed-up creeks, creating the snaking tailings piles that are Dawson's defining landscape feature.

Much of the territory had emptied out by 1953, when the capital was moved south to Whitehorse. But Yukon's brawling, big-mountain physicality has continued to tug on adventurous imaginations.

"You could definitely say I heard the call of the wild," says Scott Fleming, 42, a soft-spoken carpenter from Ontario who arrived in Dawson in 1992, chasing the promise of a life that could be both hardscrabble and good.

I get to know Fleming during a 13-day canoe expedition on the Snake River, which twists through the Bonnet Plume Range, eventually emptying into the Peel River. The Peel watershed is one of the largest still pristine river systems on Earth. Long insulated from development by its remoteness, the watershed in recent years has drawn the mining industry's attention. As First Nations and conservation groups push for protection, the Peel has become the subject of nationwide petition drives, election-year debates, and competing proposals to protect or develop the wilderness area.

Fleming ran into Ryan, also from Ontario, shortly after arriving in Dawson. Ryan had come to the Yukon in his 20s to do some fur trap-

The Yukon's brawling, big-mountain physicality has continued to tug on adventurous imaginations.

ping but quickly turned to mushroom hunting, supplying wild fungi to the lucrative international restaurant trade. Then he got hooked on gold prospecting.

In the Yukon, much of which was never glaciated, gold deposits come in two forms. So-called lode ore is held solidly in rocky veins where it was borne up through the Earth's crust. Placer gold is created when lode ore is loosened by erosion and carried away from the main ore body by water and gravity, concentrating as flecks and nuggets in streambeds and buried under gravel and sand.

"Shawn was convinced that the mother lode was still out there," Fleming tells me one night as we cook dinner by the last rays of sun. "He said that for the past hundred years people were seeing the tracks and not the beast."

Ryan hired Fleming as his first employee, and for the next six years the two men used bicycles, a beat-up wooden boat, and mostly their own feet to access promising-looking wilderness. Refining their rigorously scientific system of collecting and analyzing data, the two men began to home in on what would eventually prove to be millions of ounces of gold. But just when Ryan had persuaded his first major investors to come on board, Fleming departed to pursue a career in carpentry.

On day five of our Snake River expedition

I ask Fleming why he left on the eve of the big payoff. Our group of eight has taken a daylong break from the river to hike up to Mount Mac-Donald, a multi-spired wonderland of rock walls, glaciers, and hidden box canyons.

"Shawn's a great guy and greener than most," Fleming tells me when we stop for lunch in a high meadow sprinkled with arctic poppies. "But being out on the land every day and see-

"I tell people not to get too attached to all this beauty," says Shawn Ryan. "We just might want to mine it."

———

ing places like this, I guess it had an effect on me." He gazes out over the river and across the purple mountains that sprawl to the horizon. "I realized I didn't want to be part of tearing it up."

We follow a milky stream up the valley, springing across thick beds of sphagnum moss. We step over moose and wolf tracks and pause to watch a golden eagle making halfhearted dives toward a young Dall sheep huddled on a ledge under its mother. It's nearly midnight when we return to our riverside camp, which is newly adorned with a pile of grizzly scat.

By morning the weather has turned, dusting the surrounding mountaintops with snow. We don dry suits, tarp the canoes, and launch toward a formidable canvas of dark clouds.

The wind and rain come in hard over the next two days, raising the river and dislodging tree trunks, which we swerve to miss as we race downstream. The waterway braids through broad valleys, its branches converging and quickening to squeeze through white-water canyons. The rapids test us, tossing bucketfuls of glacial water in our faces, freezing our hands, threatening to overturn our heavy canoes as we dodge boulders and bounce through rolling wave trains.

The river serves up gifts too: fresh-caught grayling, which we cook over an alder fire. A

summit cloaked in deep red alpenglow. The camaraderie born of shared challenge in a place that's real and raw. With each day on the river we're all breathing more deeply, feeling more robust and confident.

Thus far we've seen no sign that humans have ever set foot here. And so it's jarring when, on the ninth day, we spot an oil drum lying on its side atop a strand of red rocks.

A few miles up a tributary of the Snake, one of North America's largest iron deposits was discovered in 1961. The site was test mined but never fully developed. Since then, demand for steel in Asia's emerging economies has renewed interest in the Crest Deposit, and mining industry advocates are talking of developing a rail link to the coast.

"Overland access is always the Achilles heel of wilderness," says Dave Loeks, chairman of the Peel Watershed Planning Commission. "Right now the Peel as a wilderness is as good as it gets. We'd better have a darn good reason before we develop it, because it's a one-way gate. The mining industry always makes big promises, but now we have closed mines in the Yukon that are leaking arsenic and cyanide and lead. Instead of paying to clean up the mess, the companies just go bankrupt."

But Bob Holmes, director of Mineral Resources for the Yukon government, says the industry has changed. Holmes, formerly a manager at the Faro lead-zinc mine—now the site of a more than $700 million government cleanup that will require an estimated hundred years to complete—says new bonding and reclamation policies have reduced the risk of major failures. "Nowadays you can't put a shovel in the ground until you have a closure plan."

Environmentalists say the Yukon's archaic mining laws are long overdue for an overhaul. "Mining is part of our history, and no one wants to see it go," says Lewis Rifkind, of the Yukon Conservation Society. "But the current technology can do terrible damage, and we're still regulating it with laws written when that bearded guy on our license plates was crouching in a creek, shaking a pan."

The Yukon's so-called free-entry system allows any adult to stake a claim on the majority of the territory's land—including some native lands and private property—and to use the land in virtually any way necessary to access the mineral resources below, subject to regulatory and environmental rules. Recently, however, an appeals court decision has cast doubt on the Yukon government's right to allow prospectors to explore and stake claims on some traditional lands without first consulting the affected native peoples and accommodating their rights.

The royalty rate for placer mining—37.5 cents an ounce in Canadian currency—was set in 1906, when gold was valued at $15 an ounce. From April 2012 to March 2013, Yukon placer miners produced some $70 million in gold and collectively paid $20,035 in royalties.

Yukon's premier, Darrell Pasloski, says reform of the royalty and free-entry systems is not a high priority on the government's agenda. "Placer mines are like the family farms of the Yukon," says Pasloski, whose 2011 reelection campaign was heavily supported by mining interests. "And the free-entry system creates opportunities for the little guy. A story like Shawn Ryan's wouldn't exist if you modified that."

NEARING THE END of my stay in the Yukon, I find myself back in Dawson. Gold has just topped $1,700 an ounce, and there's talk that it could break $2,000.

"People keep asking if I'm going to cash out, now that I've made my fortune," Ryan says. "I tell 'em, 'Aye, are you kidding? This is the greatest Easter egg hunt on Earth!'"

I hitch a ride on a helicopter to a promising site near the Ogilvie Mountains that Ryan's team has been exploring. As we take off, I can see up and down the fabled gold rush creeks—Bonanza, Hunker, Eldorado—where bulldozers have replaced that bearded guy shaking a pan.

Within minutes, though, I'm buzzing over mountains blanketed in thick forest and roamed by wildlife. I land in a light drizzle at a hilltop campsite, where I meet Morgan Fraughton, then one of Ryan's project managers. Guided by his GPS, Fraughton and I head out to a nearby ridge and spend the day walking a traverse line, stopping every 50 yards or so to twist a hollow auger into the ground.

The hillside, covered with moss, fireweed, and lichen, is a miracle riot of color and nutrition. Underneath the vegetation the dirt is just as colorful and diverse. Fraughton's auger brings up samples of yellow sand, bluish loam, green gravel, and red clay. "If we get data back that looks positive, it's supercrucial to get out and stake it quick," Fraughton says, as he photographs and bags the dirt. "It's like the Wild West the way rumors fly in Dawson. A couple weeks ago we went to stake an area where we'd found good soil, and someone had already staked it."

The rain tapers in the late afternoon as we make our way back to the prospectors' camp. As we descend a steep, boulder-strewn hillside, I mention something Ryan told me: "I tell people not to get too attached to all this beauty. We just might want to mine it."

Fraughton sighs. "Yeah, I can see how that kind of thing can make people nervous," he says. "But there's no guarantee that this will be mined. If it is, I hope it's done in a responsible manner. But I'm just a prospector. If I wasn't out here, someone else would be, making 300 bucks a day."

As we approach camp, the clouds begin to part, splintering the sunlight into beams that spotlight a few of the broad-shouldered mountains jostling by the hundreds toward the horizon. A half dozen summits, suddenly bathed in ethereal yellow light, begin to sparkle and steam. It's a natural spectacle on a scale so vast it seems impossible, at this moment, that any of it could ever be in short supply.

Fraughton and I sit down for a minute to pick a few blueberries and take it all in. "You know what the amazing thing is?" he says. "I've been all over this territory, and it's hard to believe, but it's this good everywhere. Wherever you go, there's just mountains and more mountains, too many to name, too many to count. And I think, What if one of them disappeared? Would it really make a difference?" □

KARMA
of the
CROWD

At the Kumbh Mela,
the largest religious festival in the world,
a throng of millions can be one.

Pilgrims wait to bathe in the early morning at the 2013 Kumbh Mela festival in Allahabad, India. In spite of polluted water and cold, crowded conditions, they report returning home healthier than they came.

PANORAMA COMPOSED OF FIVE IMAGES

The Ganges is crisscrossed with 18 pontoon bridges for festivalgoers. Below, prospective holy men head to an initiation ceremony, where they will cast off self-interest for the collective good.

Detail of the Kumbh Mela site taken in late October 2012.

AN INSTANT MEGACITY

The Kumbh Mela in Allahabad hosts many millions of pilgrims over a roughly eight-week period. To serve this massive influx, the religious festival must provide all the food, health care, and basic amenities of a major urban center. Construction on the floodplain can't get under way until November, after the waters have receded from the previous year's monsoon. Organizers have just two months to build the temporary megacity before the first inhabitants arrive in January.

Allahabad

INDIA

The same view in February 2013 during the mela.

The *sangam,* or sacred confluence of the Ganges and Yamuna Rivers

Most popular ghats, or entry points to the water, closest to the sangam

The main procession path to the sangam

A total of 18 pontoon bridges are floated into place on the Ganges.

The "city" is divided into 14 sectors, each with its own hospital, police station, roads, and power supply.

About four miles from the sangam is the Allahabad railway station, where 36 pilgrims were killed in a stampede on an overcrowded platform.

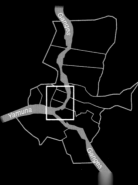

All 14 sectors of the Kumbh Mela site occupy some ten square miles. The white box marks the area shown in the satellite images above.

JOHN TOMANIO, NGM STAFF, FARHANA HOSSAIN. SATELLITE IMAGES: DIGITALGLOBE
SOURCES: SOUTH ASIA INSTITUTE, HARVARD UNIVERSITY; ALLAHABAD KUMBH MELA ADMINISTRATION

By Laura Spinney

Photographs by Alex Webb

On February 10, 2013, overcrowding at a railway station in the northern Indian city of Allahabad led to a stampede that killed 36 people. The city was full at the time. Very full. It was hosting the world's largest religious gathering, the Maha Kumbh Mela, and the authorities estimated the number of pilgrims in the city that day hit its peak, at 30 million. The stampede made headlines around the world and is what most non-Hindus remember about the festival. But there's another story about the Maha Kumbh Mela that hasn't been told.

It begins two weeks earlier, about four miles from the station, on the banks of the River Ganges. It's the second major bathing day of the festival. Dawn has yet to break, fog shrouds the river, and a full moon illuminates the crowd massing at its edge. There are thousands of people here already, but this crowd is serene, unified. There's no pushing or shoving, let alone panic—only a palpable sense of purpose as they wade in, immerse themselves in the icy water, and wade out again. People make way for each other, give each other a helping hand. The ritual complete, purpose turns to joy. "How do you feel?" I ask a man wearing a dripping loincloth. "Rejuvenated," he says, as two, then three, then four newcomers take his place.

Looking on is a policeman whose job is to keep the crowd moving, since no fewer than seven million people are expected to bathe here today. "Each one, on his own, wouldn't be able to do it," he says. "They give each other strength." His words echo my thoughts. There's an energy coming off this crowd, a sense that it amounts to more than the sum of its parts. The French 19th-century sociologist Émile Durkheim coined a phrase for it: collective effervescence. He was convinced it had a positive impact on individuals' health. His ideas were sidelined during the mass violence of the 20th century, but perhaps he was on to something. Have crowds been misunderstood?

The Indian government schedules hundreds of trains to and from Allahabad during the Kumbh. Departure seems the most stressful time: Among homeward-bound pilgrims the palpable spirit of cooperation that characterizes the festival can fray.

IN THE WEST THERE'S a pervasive idea that when people congregate, they surrender their individual identity, along with their ability to reason and behave morally—some of the very qualities that make us human.

"What our research shows is that, actually, crowds are critical to society," says psychologist Stephen Reicher of the University of St. Andrews in the United Kingdom. "They help form our sense of who we are, they help form our relations to others, they even help determine our physical well-being."

To test that idea, Reicher and his colleagues came to this place of potent cosmic significance for Hindus. It's here that the sacred Ganges meets the Yamuna and a third, mythical river called the Saraswati. Here, according to the scriptures, an ancient tussle between gods and demons led to the spilling of the nectar of immortality, or amrit. And here, a Hindu who

bathes in these rivers washes away his sins and comes a step closer to heaven.

Every year several million people make the pilgrimage to Allahabad to perform that ritual at a gathering called a mela. Every 12 years, when the alignment of the stars is considered particularly auspicious, the gathering is an order of magnitude larger, and a giant tent city rises out of the Ganges floodplain to host the Maha Kumbh Mela, or Kumbh. In 2013 the Kumbh drew an estimated 70 million people over 56 days. The mela has always excited outsiders' curiosity, mainly for its exotic processions of naked, snarling, ash-smeared holy men. Reicher and his colleagues had a different focus. They were interested in the people who came to blend with the crowd, rather than stand out from it.

Half an hour's jeep ride from the confluence of the Ganges and the Yamuna, but still within the Kumbh "city," 70-year-old Bishamber Nath Pandey and his wife, Bimla, 65, invite me into their tent. Carpets cover the dirt floor, but otherwise there's little comfort. The Pandeys are *kalpwasis*, pilgrims who come to the mela for at least a month and live a spartan lifestyle while they're here. They describe their daily routine to me: a dip before dawn, one frugal meal, chores, prayer, chanting.

"Have you ever been sick during your stay?" I ask. The kalpwasis are predominantly elderly, their tents are unheated, and the temperature at night often falls to near freezing. The Ganges, according to the local authorities' own measurements, is so polluted with sewage and industrial

---

Laura Spinney's portrait of a European city in 70 voices, Rue Centrale, *was published last year. Alex Webb's tenth book of photographs,* Memory City, *created with the photographer Rebecca Norris Webb, will be published this year.*

effluent that it is neither drinkable nor safe to bathe in (the kalpwasis do both). And thanks to a PA system that broadcasts music, religious discourses, and practical announcements on a 24-hour loop, the noise level in their camps varies from 76 to 95 decibels, high enough to cause permanent hearing loss over a prolonged period.

Pandey shakes his head. It's his 12th mela, and he always goes home in a better state of mind than when he arrived. "Living among the gods," as he puts it, helps him to forget the hardship. "My mind is healthy, so my body is too."

Before the start of the 2011 mela a colleague of Stephen Reicher's, Shruti Tewari of Allahabad University, organized a team of field workers to go out into the countryside and question 416 prospective kalpwasis about their mental and physical health. They did the same for 127 of the kalpwasis' neighbors, and they returned to administer the same questionnaires to both groups a month after the mela had finished. They also interviewed the kalpwasis during the festival, to record their experiences of it.

Their findings would have made Durkheim effervesce. Those who stayed in their villages self-reported no real change over the period of the study. The kalpwasis, on the other hand, reported a 10 percent improvement in their health, including less pain and breathlessness, less anxiety, and higher energy levels—an effect comparable to that of some powerful drugs. Antidepressants, for instance, have been estimated to reduce the public health burden of depression in some populations by about 10 percent. But as Reicher points out, antidepressants treat only depression, whereas the crowd "drug" seemed to have a positive influence on all aspects of the kalpwasis' health. What's more, the good effects last long afterward—certainly for weeks, possibly for months.

Why should belonging to a crowd improve your health? The psychologists think the cornerstone of the effect is shared identity. "You think in terms of 'we' rather than 'I,'" explains Nick Hopkins, a colleague of Reicher's from the University of Dundee in the U.K., and that in turn alters your relationship to other people: "What happens is a fundamental shift from seeing people as other to seeing them as intimate." Support is given and received, competition turns to cooperation, and people are able to realize their goals in a way they wouldn't be able to alone. That elicits positive emotions that make them not only more resilient to hardship but also healthier.

Belonging to a crowd—at least the right sort of crowd—might thus benefit the individual in the same ways more personal social connections do. We know that stress-resilience mechanisms can be activated by social interaction, with positive effects on the immune and cardiovascular systems. Very socially connected people tend to have lower levels of molecules associated with inflammation circulating in their blood, for example. They are less likely to die of heart disease and some cancers, and there's some evidence that they are less vulnerable to age-related cognitive decline. They respond better to vaccinations. Their wounds may even heal faster.

Reicher makes a critical distinction between a physical and a psychological crowd. A physical crowd—commuters jostling on a subway, for instance—lacks a shared identity. Although being very socially connected isn't the same as being physically surrounded by other people, it has a lot in common with belonging to a psychological crowd—sharing a group identity. And it isn't just bodily systems that are altered by the shift from "I" to "we."

"Belonging to the crowd can change the way you see the world," says Reicher's colleague, psychologist Mark Levine of the University of Exeter in the U.K. "It can alter your perception." In interviews kalpwasis often described the noise at the mela as blissful. "It's God's name ringing in your ears," said one. "The noise?" said another. "Oh, this is the real Saraswati."

THE RESEARCH IS TIMELY. Since the last Kumbh, in 2001, humanity has crossed a line: For the first time in history, more than half the world's population is urban. Despite the elevated levels of crime, pollution, and crowding in cities,

Why should belonging to a crowd improve your health?
The psychologists believe the cornerstone of the effect
is shared identity: thinking in terms of "we" rather than "I."

scientists talk about an "urban advantage" when it comes to health. And not just health.

In 2007 a paper in the *Proceedings of the National Academy of Sciences* made the case that as the population of a city increases, the degree of social interaction in that city increases too, only faster—with positive effects on the creation of everything from art to knowledge to wealth. "There is a 10 to 15 percent extra benefit, on average," says sociologist Dirk Helbing of the Swiss Federal Institute of Technology in Zürich, one of the paper's authors. "So there is a strong social force driving us toward living together."

Implicit in the case for an urban advantage is that the city's infrastructure must be capable of delivering it. Collective effervescence won't make people healthier if their drinking water is contaminated. The histories of both the Kumbh and the hajj, another major religious gathering, are punctured by outbreaks of communicable diseases as well as stampedes or other crowd incidents. Though these threats are ever present, improved public health measures and understanding of crowd dynamics are gradually limiting their impact.

In 2013 there were no outbreaks of serious communicable diseases in Allahabad. The Kumbh "city" covered more than ten square miles—roughly half the size of Manhattan. The inhabited area was divided into 14 sectors, each with its own hospital, police station, roads, grocery store, and supplies of electricity and drinking water—an extraordinary feat, when you think that construction couldn't get under way until the previous November, once the floodwaters had receded after the monsoon. "Incredibly well organized, incredibly clean, very efficiently run" was the verdict of Rahul Mehrotra, a professor of urban design and planning at Harvard University, who observed the festival.

The Kumbh authorities plan the layout with crowd management in mind. Exit routes from bathing places are roughly twice the width of entry routes, for example. This year the task of managing the crowd fell to Alok Sharma, inspector general of police for the Allahabad zone, who had a 14,000-strong police and paramilitary force at his command. When I met him in early February, he explained to me that his basic strategy involved shifting and dividing crowds with the use of detours to avoid buildup at hot spots.

One such hot spot was the main railway station, so the police monitored the arrival of trains. "Any crowd of 500 plus is reported because I have to make room for it," said Sharma. But he was also worried about the 18 pontoon bridges spanning the rivers. They were, in his opinion, too narrow. Where people funneled onto them, there was the potential for a crush. "We can identify the hot spots," he said, "but we can't predict when or at which one something might happen."

Nobody predicted the stampede at the train station on February 10. By the time it happened, Reicher had gone home, but I remembered an interview he and his colleagues had conducted in which a kalpwasi was asked to describe the feeling in the crowd at the station. "People think they are more powerful than you, they can push you around," she said. She was then asked to describe the feeling in the mela proper: "People are concerned about you. They treat you in a polite manner: 'Come, mother, [they say,] and go comfortably.'"

In an email from St. Andrews, Reicher wrote that one possible cause for the stampede may have been that the pilgrims no longer formed a

Before dawn an old woman performs puja, a ritual offering to the gods. The most devout pilgrims are often elderly. They come for the entire festival and renounce all comfort while there.

psychological crowd. The others around them were no longer part of a larger whole but competitors for seats on a train bound for home.

The psychologists don't deny that bad things happen in crowds. If a crowd's goal is destructive, then that is the goal it will realize. Witness the urban riots in Britain in 2011, which were characterized by looting and arson. But collective effervescence can be a powerful force for good, they argue, and that has been overlooked. In 2009, when I first met Levine, he had just completed an analysis of CCTV footage of alcohol-fueled conflict in public places in a British city. His conclusion was that bystanders played a determining role in whether a confrontation turned violent or not.

In other words, when there is the potential for violence, crowds can have a calming influence—a finding that flew in the face of previous research on the so-called bystander effect, which

suggested that some people surrender individual responsibility in a crowd, standing helpless as horrors unfold before their eyes. Between them, Reicher and his colleagues have studied religious crowds, football crowds, political parades, and music festivals.

"Living out your beliefs takes a different form in a crowd of kalpwasis than in a crowd at a rock concert," Reicher says. "But the underlying process is the same." Reporting on the opening day of the Woodstock festival in 1969, *Life* magazine quoted an official who had just realized that more people would be coming than he had anticipated. "There are a hell of a lot of us here," he said. "If we are going to make it, you had better remember that the guy next to you is your brother." They did, and the three-day festival is remembered as much for its peace and love as for its mud, food shortages, and traffic jams.

Gilded by the low afternoon sun, pilgrims drink deeply of the sacred water close to the confluence of the Ganges and Yamuna Rivers. Never mind that the water is polluted: Festivalgoers believe it contains amrit, the nectar of immortality.

"The Kumbh works because of a combination of good infrastructure and psychological cooperation," says Reicher. But in more advanced industrialized societies, the power of cooperation has been neglected, and we may be paying the price.

In the United States, for example, life expectancy has grown over the past 50 years but not as fast as it has in other developed countries. As a result American life expectancy has fallen down the world ranking, so that the United States now keeps company with Chile and Poland, which spend much less on health. One possible explanation, according to Lisa Berkman, a social epidemiologist at Harvard, is that Americans have become increasingly isolated socially. She points to evidence that the sense of community has declined. "We've lost sight of the fact that we're social animals," she says.

The message, then, is love thy neighbor, because thy neighbor will spur thee on to greater things, as Vashisht Narayan Mishra, a 69-year-old retired teacher and kalpwasi, explained to me. I had asked him how he found the courage to take the plunge on a frigid morning. "Seeing people bathe who are more aged than me inspires me," he said. "Who inspires them?" I asked. "God," he replied.

AND THERE'S THE RUB: Joining a psychological crowd is not as easy as simply wanting to belong. Looking at the brownish, fast-flowing river, and especially knowing what I do about its fecal coliform content, I cannot persuade myself that I'm looking at the nectar of immortality. Does that mean you have to be born into an identity to be able to share it? No: Conversions do happen.

Deep inside the instant city I meet Geeta Ahuja, who recounts her conversion to me. A senior finance manager with General Electric who lives in Erie, Pennsylvania, she was a "born skeptic who practiced all the vices" until she heard a Hindu sage speak in Dallas, Texas, in 2007. "He talked about the impermanence of relationships in the material world," she said. "It struck a chord with me." She became his disciple, and her life took on meaning.

"In the Bhagavad Gita," says Geeta, referring to an ancient Indian epic, "it is written that the company of people who don't believe in seeking eternal truth is bad company." Her eyes, dramatically outlined in kohl, glitter as she tries to describe how it feels to be surrounded by people who are all seeking the same thing she is. The word she hits on is "uplifted." But if the Kumbh doesn't mean anything to you, she warns, it will seem like "a kaleidoscope of nothingness, a Las Vegas, a Disneyland, just another fair."

But one can marvel at the power of collective effervescence without converting—as one man did at the mela of 1896. "It is wonderful," he wrote, "the power of a faith like that, that can make multitudes upon multitudes of the old and weak and the young and frail enter without hesitation or complaint upon such incredible journeys and endure the resultant miseries without repining." The man was an American, and his name was Mark Twain. ☐

NG CONNECT

NATIONAL GEOGRAPHIC ON TV

Brain Games

It's all in your head. That's what *Brain Games*—back for its third season—proves once again through a series of experiments, optical illusions, and riddles rooted in science. Discover why trusting others benefits society and why some people prefer to cheer for the underdog. Got a competitive streak? Learn why that's a good thing too, this month on the National Geographic Channel.

BLOG

PROOF Storytellers of all stripes discuss photography, art, and journalism on our new photo blog, Proof. Find interviews, videos, and more at *proof.nationalgeographic.com*.

LECTURE

POLAR OBSESSION An emperor penguin shooting toward the surface in a bubbly burst makes for a stunning photo (left), but what's it like on the other side of the lens? Find out from Paul Nicklen, an expert on photographing animals in extreme environments. For speaking dates and locations visit *nglive.org*.

TRIPS

TRAVEL TOGETHER Take the whole crew along on one of our family trips. Check out new itineraries for Tanzania, China, and Iceland, as well as classic expeditions to Alaska and the Galápagos, at *ngexpeditions.com/family*.

EXHIBIT

THE POWER OF PHOTOGRAPHY More than 500 images from our archive, including one of a tour guide at work in Egypt in 2011 (right), are showcased at the Annenberg Space for Photography in Los Angeles. Visit *annenbergspaceforphotography.org* for details.

Book of the Month

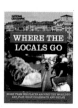

Where the Locals Go

Eat, shop, relax, and celebrate like a local even when you're new in town. This international guide, compiled by National Geographic's expert travel editors, provides insider tips on undiscovered restaurants, up-and-coming neighborhoods, street festivals, and other diversions far from the usual tourist traps. On sale February 4 ($24.95).

At Last, a Bear
Photographer Paul Nicklen waded into the frigid water of a river in the Canadian Yukon and set up a camera with a remote trigger. Then he waited for a bear to come by. He'd seen plenty of bears chasing salmon in the river, but it took 15 days before a grizzly came to inspect the shiny camera housing.

Nicklen had been drawn to the Yukon because of its beauty. He wanted to take pictures of the massive mountains and glaciers. But a gold rush started in 2011, after mineral deposits were unearthed north of Dawson, and so his coverage shifted: "It quickly turned from a pretty-picture story into an urgent one about mining a wild place."

Nicklen mingled with miners in hotels and bars, hearing their stories about why they'd come to the Yukon and the dollar signs that had attracted many of them. Away from the mines, Nicklen wanted to capture the wild spirit—and animals—of the area. After the grizzly bear wandered away, he retrieved his dry suit, which he'd propped up against a tree. It was frozen stiff from the subzero temperatures, so he stomped on it to thaw it, put it on, and went into the river to retrieve the camera. The final frame had captured a clearly inquisitive bear. —*Daniel Stone*

Listen to an interview with Paul Nicklen on our digital editions.

PHOTO: MARCO GROB (TOP)

Tall Order

In 1902, on the odd triangular lot created by the intersections of Fifth Avenue, Broadway, and 23rd Street, rose the Flatiron Building—one of New York City's early skyscrapers. Originally the building had 20 stories. A 21st floor was added in 1905.

This Fifth Avenue view of the wedge-shaped structure ran in the July 1918 issue of *National Geographic* to illustrate a story called "New York—The Metropolis of Mankind." In that article author William Joseph Showalter notes, "From whatever angle it is viewed, whatever facet throws back the light of its activities to the beholder, New York challenges one's interest and stirs one's imagination." —*Margaret G. Zackowitz*

↖ **Get Lost in Found.** Go to **NatGeoFound.tumblr.com.**

PHOTO: W. W. ROCK, NATIONAL GEOGRAPHIC CREATIVE

IS SCIENCE
COMPLICATED,
BORING,
ONLY FOR NERDS?

ENTERTAIN
YOUR BRAIN

NONE OF
THE ABOVE

See Tim Shaw take science to the streets and reveal
to everyday people why things do what they do.

Coming soon

NATIONAL
GEOGRAPHIC
CHANNEL

natgeotv.com

Marbled Polecat *(Vormela peregusna)*
Size: Body length, 27 - 38 cm; tail, 12 - 22 cm **Weight:** 260 - 520 g **Habitat:** Prefers dry, open spaces, but also lives in bushes and forest edges of semi-arid areas **Surviving number:** Unknown

Photographed by Ahmet KARATAŞ

WILDLIFE AS CANON SEES IT

Smells like trouble. When the marbled polecat is threatened, it throws its head back, displays its coloring and emits a noxious defensive odor. And if that doesn't have the desired effect, it plays dead. The elusive hunter employs offensive strategies as well, such as approaching and attacking from the side. With the help of these techniques, it can overcome prey larger than itself during its forays at dusk, dawn and throughout the night. But as its steppe habitat shrinks in Europe and Asia, the polecat may be facing more trouble than it can handle.

As Canon sees it, images have the power to raise awareness of the threats facing endangered species and the natural environment, helping us make the world a better place.

EOS System

Canon